Concepts in Biochemistry

CONCEPTS
IN BIOCHEMISTRY
A Programmed Text

William K. Stephenson
Earlham College

John Wiley & Sons, Inc.   New York ● London ● Sydney

This program was prepared pursuant to a contract with the United
States Office of Education, Department of Health, Education and
Welfare.

ISBN 0 471 82207 8
Library of Congress Catalog Card Number: 66-28762
Printed in the United States of America

PREFACE

General Purposes. This is a programmed instruction textbook which covers the chemistry and biochemistry requisite for a first course in contemporary college biology. The introductory biology course in most institutions now contains considerable emphasis on biochemistry. Yet, in most cases, beginning biology students have had neither previous college chemistry nor biochemistry. Few texts contain adequate biochemistry coverage, and it is difficult to include this material in lectures because of the variability in student background and the time required. This text is designed, therefore, to bring all students to a common level of competence in biochemistry with minimal investment of student and instructional time. Particular emphasis is placed on chemical bonding and the structural formulae which are most used in biology. The level of sophistication of the concepts covered and the pedagogy used are designed for college freshmen and sophomores.

This text is in no way a substitute for regular chemistry courses or any portion of the chemistry curriculum. Its scope is obviously not as broad and its treatments less thorough than those in conventional courses. Because it is directed toward students who may have had no previous chemical training, some concepts and treatments are over-simplified. I sincerely hope that such simplifications add clarity for the beginner and will not confuse or hinder the student who goes on to more formal chemistry training.

Assumptions as to Student Background. It is assumed that a student will bring certain skills to the task of completing this program: the ability to interpret data on a coordinate graph; competence in addition, subtraction, multiplication, division, and simple algebraic manipulations; and a minimal ability to read and understand English.

No previous training in chemistry is necessary to work through the material successfully. On the other hand, students who have had one or two years of secondary school chemistry or one year of college chemistry still find most of the program challenging. A self-test is included which will enable students with some experience to determine

which units may be omitted and which units may be studied profit-
ably.

   Time Required. Of course, the time required to complete the text
varies with the student's background and study habits. For students
who have completed the program, the average total time was about
12 hours and varied between 6 and 22 hours.

   Who Should Use this Text.   While this program is designed for
use with the introductory college biology course, it should serve other
groups equally well. A partial listing of students who should find the
text helpful includes those in introductory botany and zoology courses;
in advanced courses in genetics, cell physiology, microbiology, and
human physiology; and in preprofessional programs such as nursing,
pharmacy, medical technology, and related areas. Also those who wish
to gain a background in biochemistry can do so by studying independently.

   Suggestions to the Instructor for Use of this Text. There are several ways in which this programmed text may be used. Based on his
own experience, the author feels that it is most effective when:
   (1) Specific assignments are made and due dates set for each unit.
       The work is required and this expectation is made clear.
   (2) The completed units or text are turned in on the due date. These
       are checked off by the instructor or an assistant and returned
       immediately. They may be spot checked for completion, but
       scores or grades should not be determined or recorded.
   (3) Question-and-answer sessions are scheduled to coincide with
       the completion of the review units. These will give the students
       a chance to clear up any difficulties or ambiguities which may
       have arisen. It will also be an opportunity for the instructor to
       check informally on the level of comprehension.
   (4) Material learned in this biochemistry text is used in later com-
       ponents of the course. Such use will reinforce the initial learn-
       ing of the material and will give this new knowledge a contextual
       framework. This means that the instructor must be as familiar
       with biochemical material as his class.
   A sample schedule for textbook use might look like the one as
illustrated on the top of page v.
   If this schedule is followed, about 5 hours of outside class time
for the biochemistry work should be allowed each week.
   Alternative patterns of use might include:
   (1) Requiring all students to complete the program by a given
       date, but without compulsion. Hence there would be no due

Preceding week	Week 1		Week 2		Week 3	
	Due Day	*Unit*	*Due Day*	*Unit*	*Due Day*	*Unit*
Fri.—Assign	M	1 & 2	M	6 & 7	M	11 & 12
units, due dates,	T	3	T	8	T	13 & 14
and Q & A	W	4	W	9	W	Review
sessions	Th	5	Th	10	Th	S-1 & S-2
	F	Review	F	Review	F	Review
		Q & A		Q & A		Q & A
		session		session		session

dates for specific units, no collection of completed units, and perhaps question-and-answer sessions. Outside class time is allowed by reduction of other assignments. Students would be held responsible for the material on subsequent examinations.

(2) Assignment of the text as supplementary work, with no released time allowed. Interaction with the instructor would be at the initiation of the student. Students would be held responsible for the material on subsequent examinations.

(3) Suggesting the text as optional work. Completion of the program would not be required, and students would not be responsible for the material on examinations.

(4) Assignment of the text to be completed over the Christmas, spring, or interterm vacation periods. Opportunity for questions and discussion could be provided during the first week after the vacation.

(5) Use by individual students in independent study.

Obviously there are numerous intergrades between the patterns outlined above. The specific pattern used will ultimately depend on the judgment of each instructor with respect to the educational objectives of his course.

Following Instructions. Field tests with this program have shown that students who complete the program in writing score better on a post-test than those who do not (See field test section). If a student is to achieve the objectives which the program is designed to help him attain, it is important that he use the material in accord with the instructions. The instructor can help in this by providing a course and class structure which will facilitate using the program properly. Some means of doing this were covered in the preceding section.

Some instructors will be concerned that students may peek at the correct response before recording their answers. A few students may well do this at first. They will stop, however, as soon as they realize that the purpose of the program is to teach them rather than test them, that they themselves are the only persons who will be checking for errors, and that no one cares how many mistakes they make as long as they finally are able to demonstrate that they know what is correct.

Field Test Results. These field tests were carried out as part of an investigation to determine the most effective use of programmed instruction material (1). Within the framework of the experimental design, however, each instructor used the program as he saw fit. Students were not generally required to turn in the units, so that there was no record of the proportion of students who had or had not completed the material except in the last trial. The pre- and posttests used were slightly modified forms of the self-test contained in the next section.

Institution (2)	Test Group	Number	Pretest score	Posttest score	Retention test score
A	1	30	7.1	54.0	49.2
	2	28	8.8	59.2	51.0
	3	28	6.2	46.0	46.5
	4	18	5.5	55.7	46.3
B		30	6.2	71.7	
C		52	5.0	74.5	
D		26	19.7	51.0	
E	1	36	5.9	71.4	
	2	111	5.2	50.2	

Institution E — Group 1. All students completed the program in writing (in accordance with instructions).
Group 2. All students either did not complete the program in writing or did not complete the program.
Standard deviations on the pretest were about 7., and on the posttest and retention tests were about 16. to 18.

(1)   Field tests were supported in part by a grant from the United States Office of Education to the Great Lakes College Association under the Direction of Dr. Robert F. DeHaan, Hope College, and Dr. Donald G. Beane, College of Wooster.
(2)   The institutions participating in field testing were all private liberal arts colleges with student enrollments of less than 3000.

Suggestions to the Student for Use of this Text. This is a pro-grammed text! It is neither a test nor a speed trial nor a rote drill! Therefore, work through the material carefully and thoughtfully. Try to learn as much as you can. Ideally, you should work with the text only when you are alert and interested. Most effective learning will probably occur if you use the following procedures:

(1) Each item poses a question or asks for a response. A sample, or correct, response is listed below the item. The text re-sponse can be covered by an opaque piece of paper or card-board while you are reading an item or recording your re-sponse. A "slider" is provided with the text for this purpose.

(2) Read each item carefully and completely.

(3) Record your response to the item in the space allowed for that purpose.

(4) After completing the item, check your response with the text response. Use your best judgment in determining whether your response is sufficiently similar to the text response to indicate that you have learned the material.

(5) If you feel that your response is inadequate or incomplete, place a large "X" to the left of the item number. This will be helpful for review purposes.

(6) Then, go on to the next item; and continue to work through the text.

After the first unit or two you may feel that you can stop using the slider, or that you can stop writing down responses and just "read through" the text. While you will undoubtedly learn something if you take these short-cuts, analysis of student use of the text indicates a clear correlation between learning and adherence to the techniques outlined above. Therefore, you will learn and remember more ef-fectively if you write out responses and if you keep the text response covered until you have recorded your own response.

If you have had a strong background in chemistry or biochemistry, you may wish to skip some units. You can determine whether this is feasible by completing the appropriate items of the "self-test" in the next section.

Acknowledgments. A large number of people have contributed to the development of this program. It is literally impossible to identify each one by name here. To avoid the embarrassment of omissions let me simply express appreciation for the help of the many program-mers, colleagues, students, publishers' representatives, and clerical staff who have contributed time, talent, and criticism to the manuscript during its various stages of preparation. The writing was supported in part by a grant from the United States Office of Education to the Great Lakes College Association, under the direction of Dr. Robert F. DeHaan.

Richmond, Indiana   William K. Stephenson
October, 1966

BEHAVIORAL OBJECTIVES

As should be the case with any programmed text, *Concepts in Biochemistry* was developed and tested to teach a specified set of objectives, stated in terms of the abilities or skills the student will be able to demonstrate upon completion of each unit. The instructor can use them as a standard of measurement, both for planning his own instruction and for preparing his tests. The student may derive additional motivation for study from the realization that he has for orientation and review a convenient checklist of specific skills and terminology to be mastered rather than simply a more or less broadly subdivided table of contents to be "covered."

If he has worked through the material in accordance with the instructions, the student should be able to:

Unit 1

a. Determine the number of protons and electrons in an atom from the atomic number.
b. Determine the number of electrons in each shell for any given atom.
c. Write an outer shell diagram for any given atom.
d. Write outer shell diagrams for simple molecules and identify the covalent bonds.
e. Indicate the possible number of covalent bonds which can be formed by an atom of any given atomic number.
f. Given the written (empirical) formula for a molecule, diagram the structural formula. (e.g., ethanol, glycine)
g. Identify double bonds in outer shell diagrams.
h. Diagram double bonds in structural formulae.

Unit 2

a. Identify or diagram the structural formula for each of the following groupings of atoms: hydrocarbons, methyl and ethyl groups; hydroxyl; aldehyde; organic acid, carboxyl; keto; amino; phosphate; ester linkage; aromatic, benzene ring.

Unit 3

a.   Define an ion.
b.   Given the atomic number, write the symbol for any given ion.
c.   Identify cations and anions.
d.   Define a salt.
e.   Identify organic acids and salts from the name; identify the word
     ending characteristic of organic acids and salts.
f.   Identify the ions which are produced when a salt dissociates.
g.   Write the equation for the dissociation of a salt.

Unit 4

a.   Identify and label dipolar charges within the structural formula
     for a molecule.
b.   Diagram a hydrogen bond between two atoms.
c.   Define a hydrogen bond.
d.   Identify the common groupings of atoms which can form hydrogen
     bonds.
e.   Identify groups which will enhance the solubility of a molecule in
     water.
f.   Given structural formulae, identify groups which will form hydro-
     phobic bonds.
g.   Define hydrophobic bonding.

Unit 5

a.   Identify the products and reactants for any given reaction.
b.   Define chemical equilibrium.
c.   Add an appropriate relative rate arrow to a reaction equation to
     indicate the effect of changing the concentration of either reac-
     tants or products on the relative reaction rates.
d.   State LeChatelier's Principle.
e.   To indicate, in a reaction equation, what effect a change in the
     concentration of one component will have on the concentration of
     all other components in the reaction (increase or decrease).

Unit 6

a.   Write the empirical formula for a carbohydrate of any given car-
     bon length.
b.   Write the word ending characteristic of sugars.
c.   Identify the number of carbons from the name of a sugar (e.g.
     pentose).
d.   Write the structural formulae for lactic acid and pyruvic acid.

e. Write the structural formula and a shorthand structural formula for glucose.
f. Differentiate and identify the structural formulae for glucose and galactose.
g. Write the structural formula and shorthand structural formula for fructose.

Unit 7

a. Write the shorthand structural formulae for ribose and deoxyribose.
b. State the difference between alpha glucose and beta glucose.
c. State the difference between an alpha and a beta linkage.
d. Identify alpha and beta linkages in structural formulae.
e. List the monosaccharides produced upon hydrolysis of sucrose, maltose, lactose, and cellobiose; also to indicate which of the foregoing contain beta linkages.
f. Define a polysaccharide.
g. On the structural formulae of polysaccharides, identify 1,4 and 1,6 linkages.
h. Identify the structural formula for glucosamine.
i. List the monosaccharide units, linkages, and biological functions of amylose, glycogen, chitin, cellulose, and amylopectin.

Unit 8

a. Diagram the general structural formula for an amino acid.
b. List the seven classes of amino acids.
c. Given the structural formula for an amino acid, place it in the proper class.
d. Given a list of the 21 common amino acids, place each amino acid in the proper class.
e. Given the name of any amino acid, place it in the proper class.

Unit 9

a. Diagram the formation of a peptide bond.
b. Write the general structural formula for a polypeptide (e.g. pentapeptide) and identify each peptide unit and peptide bond.
c. Given the primary structure diagram of a protein (e.g. insulin), identify by name each amino acid and each disulfide bond.
d. State the approximate molecular weight range for proteins.
e. Given a paper model of a polypeptide (see text), construct an alpha helix.

f. Describe the alpha helix structure.
g. Identify the man (Dr. Linus Pauling) who first set forth the struc-
    ture of the alpha helix.

Unit 10

a. Define the primary, secondary, tertiary, and quaternary structure
    of proteins.
b. List the two factors involved in primary structure.
c. List the types of bonding involved in the tertiary structure of a
    protein.
d. List the types of bonding involved in the quaternary structure of a
    protein.
e. Given the definition, state the terms: simple protein, conjugated
    protein, and prosthetic group.
f. Define denaturation of a protein.
g. Define a basic protein.

Unit 11

a. Diagram the structural formula of a fat.
b. Diagram the general structural formula for a phospholipid.
c. Diagram and label the fundamental structure of a biological mem-
    brane (using abbreviated structural diagrams for the molecules
    involved).
d. Identify the hydrophobic and hydrophylic components of a mem-
    brane diagram.
e. Diagram the basic ring structure of a steroid.
f. Define a sterol.
g. List three major biological functions of sterols.
h. Identify the hydrophobic and hydrophylic portions of a sterol
    molecule.

Unit 12

a. Given the structural formulae, differentiate between a purine and
    a pyrimidine.
b. Given the names, adenine, cytosine, guanine, thymine, and uracil,
    identify each as either a purine or a pyrimidine.
c. State the three components of which a nucleotide is composed.
d. Construct a shorthand structural formula diagram for adenosine
    monophosphate, given the structural formula for adenosine.
e. Using a shorthand notation for nucleotide structure, diagram the
    structure of a nucleic acid chain.

f.   Label the backbone chains in a diagram of double stranded DNA.
g.   Given the structural formulae, diagram the hydrogen bonds which could form between adenine and thymine and between cytosine and guanine.
h.   Add the complementary chain to a diagram of single stranded DNA, including all interchain hydrogen bonds.
i.   Add the complementary RNA chain to a diagram of single stranded DNA, including all interchain hydrogen bonds.
j.   List three differences between DNA and RNA.
k.   Give the name "Watson-Crick double helix" for the helical model of DNA structure.
l.   Write the shorthand structural formula for ATP.
m.   Give the chief biological function of ATP.
n.   Complete partially finished equations involving ATP, ADP, AMP, P, and water.

Unit 13

a.   Define potential and kinetic energy.
b.   Convert between Calories and calories, and vice versa.
c.   Define an exothermic and an endothermic reaction.
d.   Given a reaction which is clearly exothermic or endothermic, state whether the reactants or products are present in greatest concentration at equilibrium.
e.   State the effect of an enzyme on a chemical reaction.
f.   List three types of bonding involved in enzyme-substrate complexing.
g.   State the function and mode of action of an enzyme.

Unit 14

a.   State what type of chemical material each of the following is composed of: plant cell wall, arthropod exoskeleton, hair, silk, genes, leather, plant starch.
b.   State the type of protein which is usually found H-bonded to the DNA of the chromosomes.

Unit S-1

a.   Given the atomic weight and atomic number of an atom, determine the number of neutrons.
b.   Given the formula for a molecule (e.g. NaOH) calculate the molecular weight and gram molecular weight.
c.   Using a table of atomic weights, calculate the number of grams of a substance in a given volume of given molarity.

d.   Outline the procedure to be followed in preparing a given volume
     of a solution of a given molarity.
e.   Outline the procedure as in "d" for molecules which have water
     of hydration in the crystal structure.

Unit S-2

a.   State the meaning of the symbol $[OH^-]$.
b.   Relate acidity and basicity to the concentration of an acid.
c.   Convert powers of 10 to numbers (e.g. $10^8 = ?$).
d.   Define the logarithm of a number.
e.   State the log to the base 10 of a multiple of 10 (e.g. log 100 = ?).
f.   Using a simple table of logarithms, calculate the logarithm of any
     given number.
g.   Convert log reciprocal to $-\log$.
h.   State the logs of 8, 5, 3, and 2 from memory.
i.   Calculate the pH for any given concentration of a strong acid.
j.   Define pH.
k.   Calculate the pH for any given concentration of a strong base.
l.   List the components of a buffer system and explain how a buffer
     system functions to resist changes in pH.
m.   Write the Henderson-Hasselbach equation and identify it by name.
n.   Given a list of weak acids and their respective pK's, choose the
     appropriate acid and its salt for a buffer system at a given pH.

SELF-TEST

This test can be used either as a pretest, to determine whether a student may omit certain units, or as a posttest to assess learning after the program has been completed. The unit containing the material covered by each question is listed at the left to facilitate pretest selection of items. Evaluation of responses will require judgment and should be conservative, that is, if there is question about the adequacy of a response it should be scored as incorrect. Emphasis should be placed on the correctness of concepts rather than upon identity of words or phrases.

For pretest use, locate the appropriate items by scanning the unit notations at the left of the test questions. Answer all questions for the given unit you wish to check. For example, if you feel that you probably know the material in Unit 1, answer questions #1 and #2. Check your responses against the key, following the instructions at the beginning of the key. If you judge your responses to be correct, you may omit that unit. If you are in doubt about your answers, you should probably work through the material in the appropriate unit to be certain of your comprehension.

SELF-TEST FOR UNITS 1-14

Unit	Question
1	1. Write the outer shell diagram for the magnesium atom (atomic number = 12).
1	2. Write the structural formula for $(CH_3CHOHCOOH)$.

Unit	Question

2

3. Match the following: A. $H-\underset{\underset{H}{\mid}}{\overset{\overset{H}{\mid}}{C}}-\underset{\underset{H}{\mid}}{\overset{\overset{H}{\mid}}{C}}-$ F. $-\underset{\underset{H}{\mid}}{\overset{\overset{H}{\mid}}{C}}-H$

  G aldehyde
  B aromatic
  C ester linkage   B. ⬡
  D keto   G. $-C\overset{\displaystyle O}{\underset{\displaystyle H}{\diagup}}$
  A ethyl

C. $-\overset{\overset{\displaystyle O}{\|}}{C}-O-$ H. $-N\overset{\displaystyle H}{\underset{\displaystyle H}{\diagup}}$

D. $-C-\overset{\overset{\displaystyle O}{\|}}{C}-C-$

E. $-C\overset{\displaystyle O}{\underset{\displaystyle OH}{\diagup}}$ I. $-O-\overset{\overset{\displaystyle O}{\|}}{\underset{\underset{\displaystyle OH}{\mid}}{P}}-OH$

J. $-OH$

3

4. Write the structural formula for sodium acetate. Indicate the ionic bond with an arrow.

acetic acid $= H-\underset{\underset{H}{\mid}}{\overset{\overset{H}{\mid}}{C}}-C\overset{\displaystyle O}{\underset{\displaystyle OH}{\diagup}}$ + NaOH

3

5. Write the *symbols* for the calcium (atomic number = 20) and chloride (atomic number = 17) *ions*.

4

6. Diagram a hydrogen bond between an $-NH_2$ group and a

$-C\overset{\displaystyle O}{\underset{\displaystyle OH}{\diagup}}$ group.

4

7. Define a hydrophobic bond.

5

8. Define chemical equilibrium for a reversible reaction.

5

9. In the reaction sequence:
    $ADP + Ph \rightleftharpoons ATP + Cr \rightleftharpoons CrPh + ADP$
    What effect would an increase in the concentration of Ph have on the concentration of CrPh? Explain briefly.

Unit   Question

6   10. Write the complete structural formula for glucose.

7   11. Match the following:
         _____ fructose
         _____ ribose
         _____ lactose
         _____ galactose
         _____ maltose
         _____ one molecule with
               a beta linkage
         _____ all disaccharides
         _____ any one pentose

(H. and I. appear on the next page.)

Unit   Question

lactose

H.

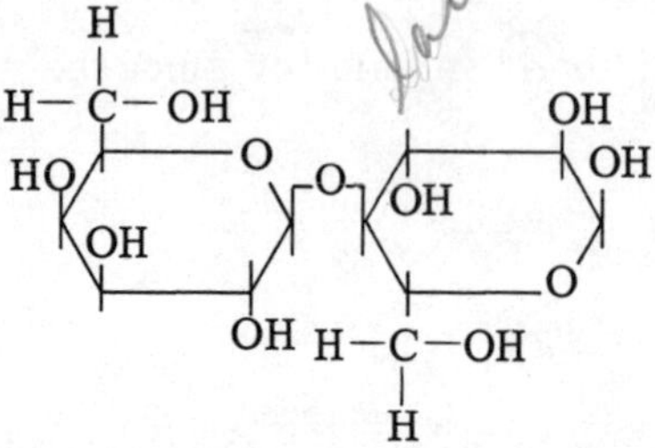

I.

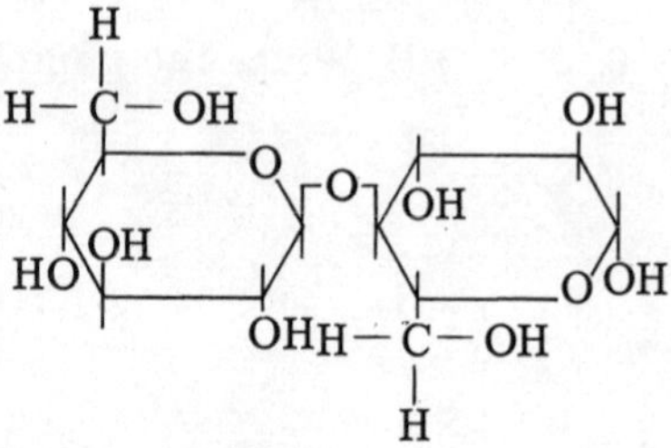

2   12. Write the structural formula for a carboxyl (acid) group.

2   13. Write the structural formula for an ester linkage.

8   14. To what group does each of the following amino acids belong?

_____

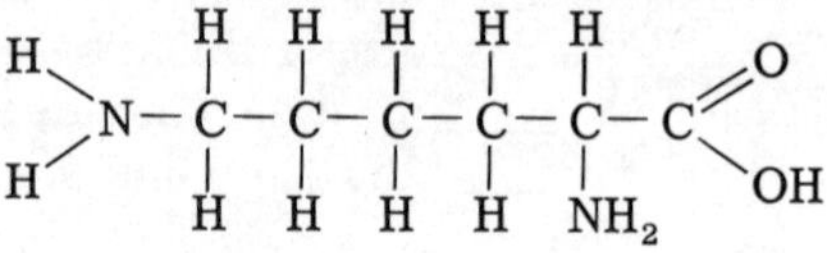

_____

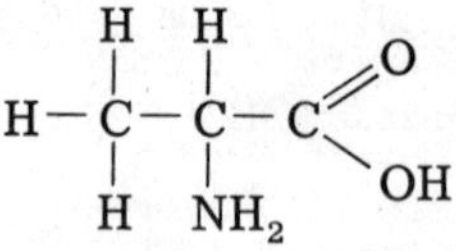

_____

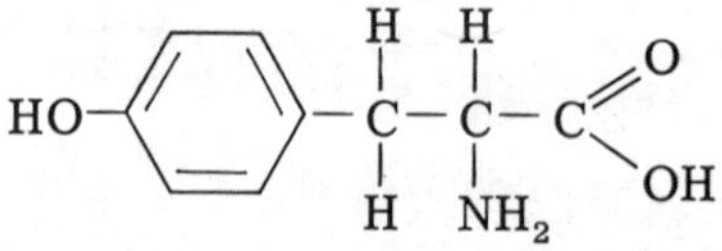

_____

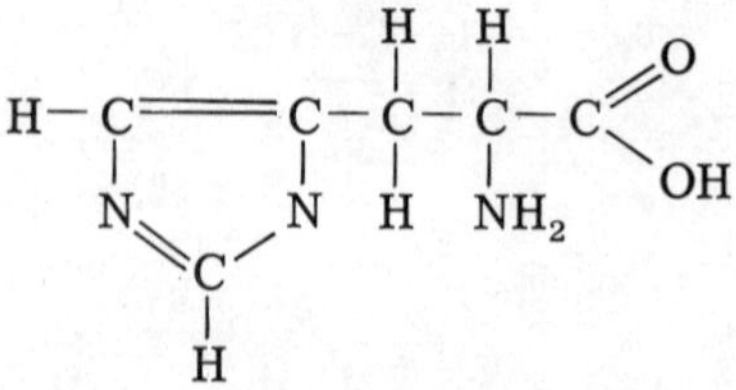

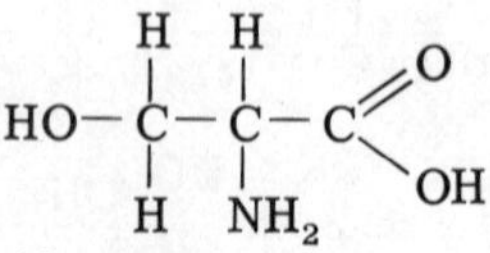

_____ Alanine
_____ Cysteine
_____ Lysine
_____ Phenylalanine

Unit	Question

9   15. *Diagram* the *general* structural formula of a tripeptide. Circle each peptide unit.

9   16. Describe briefly the structure of the alpha helix.

10.   17. Define or explain the primary structure of a protein.

10   18. What is denaturation (briefly)?

11   19. Diagram and label the basic structure of a biological membrane.

11   20. Write the general structural formula of a phospholipid.

Unit	Question
11 12	21. Match the following: _____ purine (Unit 12) _____ sterol (Unit 11) _____ pyrimidine (Unit 12)

A. 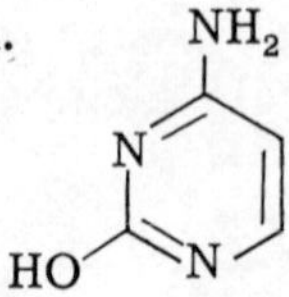

B. 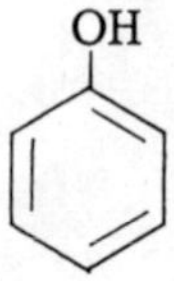

C. 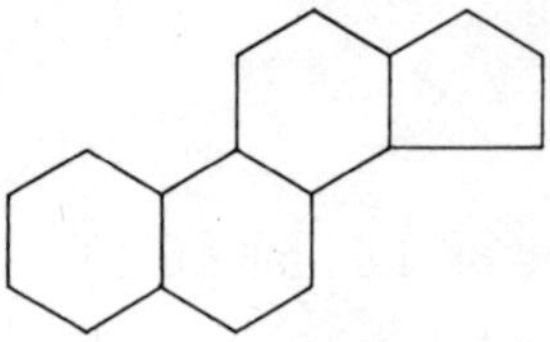

D. 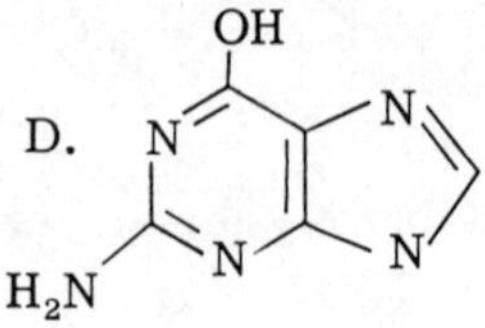

E. 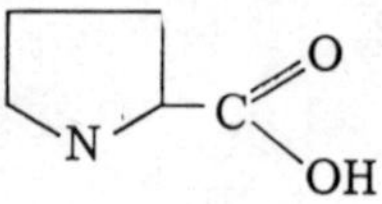

12 22. List the three constituents of a nucleotide.

12 23. Construct the *RNA* strand complementary to this DNA strand (include H bonds).

```
etc. —P—D—P—D—P—D—P—D—P—D— etc.
        |     |     |     |     |
        C     A     T     G     T
```

9 24. _____ Which man first postulated the structure of the alpha helix?

_____ Which two men first postulated the helical structure of DNA?

A. Beadle	E. Pasteur
B. Crick	F. Pauling
C. Darwin	G. Schleiden
D. Linneas	H. Watson

13 25. In the reaction: AMP + Ph + Cal. ⇌ ADP + H_2O

a. At equilibrium will AMP or ADP be present in the greatest concentration? Explain your answer briefly.

b. Is the reaction to the right probably endothermic or exothermic?

c. How many calories does 10 Calories equal?

Unit	Question
13	26. What three types of bonding are involved in enzyme-substrate binding (complexing)?
14	27. What type of protein is usually bonded to chromosomal DNA?
6 3 3	28. To what group does each of the following belong? _____ ribul*ose* (Unit 6) _____ mal*ate* (Unit 3) _____ propion*ic* (Unit 3)

SELF-TEST FOR UNITS S-1 AND S-2

Unit	Question
S-1	1. Outline the procedure you would use to prepare 100 ml. of a 0.5 molar solution of $KHCO_3$.

Atomic weights
K = 39.
H = 1.
C = 12.
O = 16.

S-2	2. Explain the meaning of the "pH" of a solution.

S-3	3. What concentration of NaOH would give a pH of 12.3?

Unit   Question

S-2   4. Write a complete definition or explanation of a buffer
             system.

SELF-TEST KEY

To facilitate scoring, a suggested breakdown of point assignments is given at the right of each correct response. The total points for each response are listed at the left margin. In evaluating your responses, use your best judgment. Remember, your evaluations should be rigorous and should stress the correctness of concepts rather than the use of identical wording. Based on previous posttest results, a score of above 50 is satisfactory and a score above 70 is quite good.

KEY FOR UNITS 1-14

Points	Responses
3	1. $\cdot$Mg$\cdot$ (Mg nucleus — 1 point; electrons — 1 point; position of electrons — 1 point)

3   2.

$$H-\overset{\overset{\displaystyle H}{|}}{\underset{\underset{\displaystyle H}{|}}{C}}-\overset{\overset{\displaystyle H}{|}}{\underset{\underset{\displaystyle OH}{|}}{C}}-C\overset{\displaystyle O}{\underset{\displaystyle OH}{<}}$$

(1 point off for each error, to a maximum of -3)

5   3.

     __G__ aldehyde
     __B__ aromatic
     __C__ ester linkage
     __D__ keto
     __A__ ethyl
(1 point each)

Points	Responses

2   4.

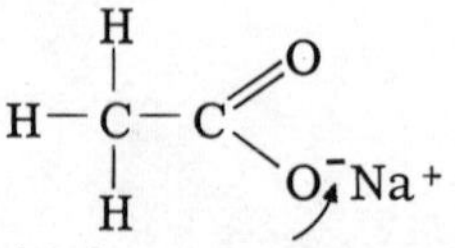

$$H-\overset{\overset{\displaystyle H}{|}}{\underset{\underset{\displaystyle H}{|}}{C}}-C\overset{\displaystyle O}{\underset{\displaystyle O^{-}Na^{+}}{\diagup}}$$

(Na$^+$ — correct position and charge — 1 point; arrow indicating ionic bond — 1 point)

4   5. $Ca^{++}Cl^{-}$
(1 point for each correct sign, + or −; 1 point for the correct number of charges)

3   6.

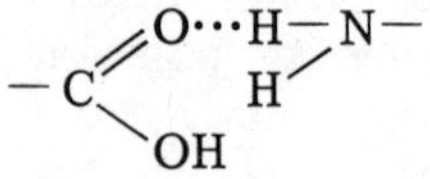

$$-C\overset{\displaystyle O\cdots H-N-}{\underset{\displaystyle OH}{\diagup}} \; \overset{\displaystyle H}{\diagup}$$

(involvement of =O, 1 point; involvement of H, 1 point; use of $\cdots$ for the hydrogen bond, 1 point)

3   7. Hydrophobic bonding involves the clustering together of hydrocarbon groups in an aqueous medium.
(1 point each for the mention of hydrocarbons, clustering, and the aqueous medium)

2   8. At equilibrium the rate of the reaction to the right equals the rate of the reaction to the left (the rate of the forward reaction equals the rate of the reverse reaction).
(1 point for the mention of rates and 1 point for mentioning equality)

3   9. The concentration of CrPh would *increase*. (1 point) An increase in the Ph concentration causes the rate of the reaction to the right to increase; this would cause the concentration of ATP to increase; this would cause the next reaction rate to the right to increase and would increase the concentration of CrPh and ADP. (1 point)
(The explanation might also be based on mass action, equilibrium constants, or a statement of LeChatelier's principle.)

Points	Response

5   10.

(1 point each for: 6 carbons, carbons in a ring, oxygen in the ring correctly, the position of the OH groups, and the attachment of the CH_2OH group)

8   11.

C	fructose		G	maltose
D	ribose		H or I	one molecule with
H	lactose			a beta linkage
B	galactose		F, G, H, I	all disaccharides
			D or E	any one pentose

(1 point for each blank — no more than 1 point per item part wrong = all wrong)

3   12.

(1 point each for the correct position of $-C$, $=O$, and $-OH$)

3   13.

(1 point each for the correct position of $-C-$, $=O$, and $-O-$)

9   14.   basic   hydrocarbon
            hydrocarbon   sulfur-containing
            aromatic   basic
            heterocyclic   aromatic
            hydroxy
            (1 point each)

Points	Responses

3   15.

(1 point each for the correct arrangement of the N—C—C etc. chain; =O; and R's and H's. R, H, and =O can be written above or below the N—C—C etc. chain. One point off for each incorrect circle.)

3   16. The alpha helix is a tight coil in a polypeptide (protein) chain. The coil is stabilized by hydrogen bonding between peptide units that are relatively close together (within 5 peptide units) on the chain.
(1 point each for mention of polypeptide or protein, hydrogen bonds, and bonding between close peptide units)

2   17. The primary structure of a protein is the specific sequence of amino acids in the polypeptide chain. It also includes disulfide (S—S) bonds between cysteine (or within cystine) units.
(1 point each for mentioning specific sequence of amino acids and disulfide or S—S bonds)

3   18. Denaturation is an alteration of the tertiary structure of a protein resulting in the loss of biological activity. It is frequently due to the disruption of hydrogen bonds. Agents commonly causing denaturation are heat, organic solvents, acids, and bases.
(1 point each for mention of alteration of tertiary structure, disruption of hydrogen bonds, and one or more agents)

5   19.

(1 point each for the ∿∿∿∿ layers, ⊓ layers, protein labels, phospholipid labels, and a bonus point for a completely correct diagram)

Points   **Responses**

3   20.

$$
\begin{array}{c}
\text{H} \\
| \\
\text{H}-\text{C}-\text{O}-\overset{\overset{\displaystyle O}{\|}}{\text{C}}-R_f \\
| \\
\text{H}-\text{C}-\text{O}-\overset{\overset{\displaystyle O}{\|}}{\text{C}}-R_f \\
| \\
\text{H}-\text{C}-\text{O}-\overset{\overset{\displaystyle O}{\|}}{\text{P}}-\text{O}-R_s \\
| \qquad | \\
\text{H} \qquad \text{OH}
\end{array}
\qquad \text{or} \qquad
\begin{array}{c}
\text{H} \\
| \\
\text{H}-\text{C}-\text{FA} \\
| \\
\text{H}-\text{C}-\text{FA} \\
| \\
\text{H}-\text{C}-\text{Ph}-R_s \\
| \\
\text{H}
\end{array}
$$

(1 point each for — glycerol — indicated by the dotted circle. — R_f or FA groups — Ph and R_s groups)

3   21.   <u>D</u> purine
         <u>C</u> sterol
         <u>A</u> pyrimidine
         (1 point each)

3   22. phosphate
         pentose sugar
         nitrogen base (purine, pyrimidine)
         (1 point each)

5   23. P—D—P—D—P—D—P—D—P—D—
             | | | | |
             C   A   T   G   T
            ⋮⋮⋮   ⋮⋮⋮   ⋮⋮⋮   ⋮⋮⋮   ⋮⋮⋮
             G   U   A   C   A
             | | | | |
         P—R—P—R—P—R—P—R—P—R—
         (1 point off for each error up to a maximum total of −5 points)

3   24.   <u>F</u>
           <u>B & H</u>
           (1 point each)

4   25. a. AMP (1 point)
         b. The energy of activation for the reaction to the right is greater than that for the reaction to the left (or similar response). (1 point)
             endothermic (1 point)
         c. 10,000 (1 point)

<u>Points</u>   <u>Responses</u>

3   26. hydrogen
              ionic (or metal complexing)
              hydrophobic
              (1 point for each correct answer)

1   27. basic (1 point)

3   28. sugar
              salt
              acid
              (1 point each)

100 POINTS TOTAL

KEY FOR UNITS S-1 AND S-2:

5   1. Molecular weight of $KHCO_3$:
              K — 39.
              H — 1.
              C — 12
              3O — 48
                   $\overline{100}$ gram M.W. = <u>100 grams</u> (1 point)
              Calculation: 1 liter of 1 M. $KHCO_3$ = 100 g/liter
                            1 liter of 0.5 M. $KHCO_3$ = 50 g/liter
                            100 ml. of 0.5 M. $KHCO_3$ = <u>5 g/100 ml.</u>
                            (2 points)
              Procedure: Obtain a 100 ml. volumetric flask.
                           Weigh out 5.0 grams of $KHCO_3$; place in the
                             flask.
                           Add about 80 ml. of distilled water.
                           Swirl flask until all the $KHCO_3$ is dissolved.
                           Add distilled water to the 100 ml. line. Mix.
                           (2 points)

3   2. The pH of a solution is the $-\log$ (or log of the reciprocal
              or log 1/conc.) of the hydrogen ion concentration.
              (1 point for mention of the hydrogen ion concentration
              2 points for using $-\log$ or log 1/concentration)

Points   **Responses**

5   3. Calculation: $pOH = \log \dfrac{1}{(OH^-)} = \log \dfrac{1}{(NaOH)} = 1.7$

pH + pOH = 14

$$pOH = 1.0 + 0.7$$

12.3 + pOH = 14

$$= \log 10 + \log 5 \ (\log 5 = 0.7$$

pOH = 14 − 12.3

from memory)

pOH = 1.7 (2 points)

$$= \log (10 \times 5) = \log (0.5 \times 10^2)$$

$$= \log \left(\frac{1}{2} \times \frac{1}{10^{-2}} \right) = \log \left(\frac{1}{2 \times 10^{-2}} \right)$$

$(OH^-) = \underline{0.02\,M.}$ (3 points)

(The above methods of calculations are examples. Any
method which yields the correct answers is acceptable.)

5   4. A buffer system contains a weak acid plus a salt anion
of that acid. The buffer system resists a change in pH
(H ion concentration); the H^+ from the acid reacts with
excess OH^-, and the salt anion reacts with excess H^+.
The buffer system will be most effective when pH = pK
(of the weak acid).
(1 point each for mention of the weak acid, salt anion,
H^+ from the acid reacting with excess OH^-, salt anion
reacting with excess H^+, and pH = pK.)

18 POINTS TOTAL

CONTENTS

Concepts in Biochemistry

UNIT *1* ATOMS AND MOLECULES

As a background for understanding bonding you will learn to relate the number of electrons and protons of an atom to the atomic number, to assign the electrons to appropriate shells, and to predict which atoms can share electrons to form covalent bonds. You will also learn to write the structural chemical formulae for simple molecules. Structural formula diagrams are widely used in biology to illustrate the atomic relationships within the large molecules characteristic of living organisms.

Material Covered

Fundamental particles — electrons, neutrons, protons
Atomic number
Electron shells
Outer shell diagrams of atoms
Electron sharing — covalent bonds
Structural formulae
Double bonds

Follow the instructions in the section *Suggestions to the Student for Use of this Text* (page ix). Take out the slider. Go on to the first item; covering the bottom of the sheet and response with the slider.

PANEL A

This material should be used for items 1-26 of Unit 1.

Table A.1

Atomic Name	Atomic Symbol	Atomic Number	Atomic Name	Atomic Symbol	Atomic Number
Argon	Ar	18	Lithium	Li	3
Beryllium	Be	4	Magnesium	Mg	12
Boron	B	5	Neon	Ne	10
Calcium	Ca	20	Nitrogen	N	7
Carbon	C	6	Oxygen	O	8
Chlorine	Cl	17	Phosphorus	P	15
Fluorine	F	9	Potassium	K	19
Helium	He	2	Sodium	Na	11
Hydrogen	H	1	Sulfur	S	16

This list is incomplete and includes only those atoms which will be used subsequently. Some atomic symbols are based on the Latin names; e.g. K (kalium) and Na (natrium).

Table A.2

Shell Number	Maximum Electrons per Shell
1	2
2	8(10)
3	8(10)
4	

Eight electrons is the usual maximum number; 10 is sometimes the maximum number.

1. Atoms are composed of *fundamental particles*: protons, neutrons and electrons. An atom can be subdivided into a central *nucleus* (containing *protons* and *neutrons*) and surrounding *electrons*. The atomic number indicates the number of protons within the nucleus. How many *protons* are in each of the following atomic nuclei?

   H_____   K_____   F_____

   C_____

   Record your responses, then move the slider down to uncover the responses.

   H_____1_____   K_____19_____   F_____9_____

   C_____6_____

   Check your response, then go on to the next item.

   _____

2. The number of electrons characteristic of an atom is equal to the number of protons. How many *electrons* are found in each atom?

   He_____   Ar_____   Li_____

   Cl_____

   Check your responses when you have finished.

   He_____2_____   Ar_____18_____   Li_____3_____

   Cl_____17_____

   _____

3. What is the number of each of the following in a phosphorus atom?

     Electrons _____

     Protons _____

- -

     Electrons ___15___

     Protons ___15___

4. Within an atom the electrons are considered to be arranged in a series of *shells* or layers. Look at Panel A, Table A.2. Note that the number of electrons in each shell does not normally exceed the maximum number listed in Table A.2. The inner (first) shells fill first. How many electrons are in each shell of a nitrogen atom?

     shell 1 _____   shell 2 _____

     shell 3 _____   shell 4 _____

- -

     shell 1 ___2___   shell 2 ___5___

     shell 3 ___0___   shell 4 ___0___

5. How many electrons are in each shell in the following atoms:

	shell 1	shell 2	shell 3	shell 4
oxygen				
phosphorous				
potassium				

- -

	shell 1	shell 2	shell 3	shell 4
oxygen	2	6	0	0
phosphorous	2	8	5	0
potassium	2	8	8	1

6. When considering the combination of atoms to form molecules, we need only be concerned with the number of electrons in the outer shell.

	Number of Electrons in Each Shell				Number of Electrons in Outer Shell	Outer Shell Diagram
	1	2	3	4		
H	1				1	H ·
He	2				2	· He ·
Li	2	1			1	Li ·
Be	2	2				Be

(Electrons are first placed at each side of the symbol)

Complete the table and write the outer shell diagram for beryllium (Be).

2	· Be ·

7.

	Number of Electrons in Each Shell				Number of Electrons in Outer Shell	Outer Shell Diagram
	1	2	3	4		
B	2	3			3	·B· (The third
C	2	4			4	·C· and fourth electrons
N	2	5			5	·N· are placed
O	2	6			6	·O· above and below the
F						symbols)
Ne	2	8			8	:Ne:

Complete the table and write the outer shell diagram for fluorine.

Extra electrons above 4 in the outer shell are added to produce pairs — *top and bottom first*.

(Shells) 2 7	7	:F· (or ·F:

8. Write the outer shell diagram for sulfur.

$\cdot \ddot{\underset{..}{S}} \cdot$ (2 6) ($:\ddot{S}:$ or $:\underset{..}{\ddot{S}}$ etc. should be avoided).

---

9. Write the outer shell diagram for Mg.

$\cdot$ Mg $\cdot$

---

10. As atoms combine, the most stable electron configuration is one in which the outer shell contains the maximum number of electrons (Table A.2). Thus, in combining, atoms may share electrons so that *the outer shell is filled.* In the diagram, circle each of the two electrons from the O atom which can be shared with the two H atoms.

---

11. Each *pair* of shared electrons is a *covalent bond,* which "holds" the two adjacent atoms together. In the right-hand diagram circle the three covalent bonds.

Example: H ⊙ $\ddot{\underset{..}{O}}$ ⊙ H

The circled electrons are shared between H and O.

$$H : \ddot{\underset{..}{N}} : H$$
with H above N

$$H ⊙ \underset{..}{N} ⊙ H$$
with H and ⊙ above N

12. In this diagram, note that each outer electron shell is filled by the sharing of electrons.

(H ⋮ O ⋮ H)   H — 2 electrons each in the outer shell
                     O — 8 electrons in the outer shell.

For each atom in this diagram, how many electrons are in the outer shell?

Each H _____   H:C:O:H (with H below C)
    O _____
    C _____

- -

Each H ___2___
    O ___8___
    C ___8___

---

13. Draw an outer shell diagram showing the combination of one C and four H atoms.

- -

        H
    H:C:H
        H

---

14. Circle the covalent bonds in your previous answer.

- -

15. A stable group of two or more atoms associated thru bonding is termed a molecule. Construct an outer shell diagram of a water molecule (H + H + O) or (H$_2$O).

H : Ö : H

16. Two atoms of hydrogen and one atom of sulfur can combine by covalent bonding to produce a molecule of hydrogen sulfide. Diagram the outer shell structure of the molecule.

H : S̈ : H

17. On the diagram of your previous answer, circle the pairs of electrons involved in covalent bonds.

H⊙S̈⊙H

18. Complete the following table.

Outer Shell Diagram	Number of Possible Covalent Bonds	
H·	1	H—
·Ö·	2	—O—
·C·	4	—C—
:N·		
·S·		

[Each (−) represents a possible covalent bond.]

Outer Shell Diagram	Number of Possible Covalent Bonds	
:N̈·	3	N—
·S̈·	2	—S—

19. Because outer shell diagrams are laborious, it is convenient to indicate each pair of shared electrons (covalent bond) by a simple dash (−) and to ignore unshared electrons.

Examples: H−S−H   or $\begin{array}{c} \quad\;\, H \\ \quad\;\, | \\ H-C-O-H \\ \quad\;\, | \\ \quad\;\, H \end{array}$

This is a *structural formula*. Write the structural formula for water (H + O + H).

- -

H−O−H

_____

20. Write the number of possible covalent bonds for each of the following:

H_____   Check your answer; then memorize
O_____   this list for later use in writing
S_____   structural formulae.
N_____
C_____

- -

H___1___
O___2___
S___2___
N___3___
C___4___

_____

21. How many covalent bonds can each of the following atoms form?

C_____   O_____   H _____
N_____   S_____

- -

C____4____   O____2____   H____1____
N____3____   S____2____

_____

22. Write the *structural formula* for methane (C + 4H) or (CH$_4$).

$$
\begin{array}{c}
\quad\ \text{H} \\
\quad\ | \\
\text{H} - \overset{\displaystyle |}{\underset{\displaystyle |}{\text{C}}} - \text{H} \\
\quad\ \text{H}
\end{array}
$$

---

23. Diagram the structural formula for methyl alcohol (CH$_3$OH). Begin with the first "C", then use the atoms from left to right.

$$
\begin{array}{c}
\quad\ \text{H} \\
\quad\ | \\
\text{H} - \overset{|}{\underset{|}{\text{C}}} - \text{O} - \text{H} \\
\quad\ \text{H}
\end{array}
\qquad \text{Note:}
$$

CH$_3$ O H

H

H — C — O — H

H

---

24. Write the structural formula for ethyl alcohol (CH$_3$CH$_2$OH).

$$
\begin{array}{c}
\quad\ \text{H}\ \ \text{H} \\
\quad\ |\ \ \ | \\
\text{H} - \overset{|}{\underset{|}{\text{C}}} - \overset{|}{\underset{|}{\text{C}}} - \text{O} - \text{H} \\
\quad\ \text{H}\ \ \text{H}
\end{array}
$$

CH$_3$ CH$_2$ O H

---

25. In some molecules, electrons are shared in groups of *four* rather than in pairs (note circles).

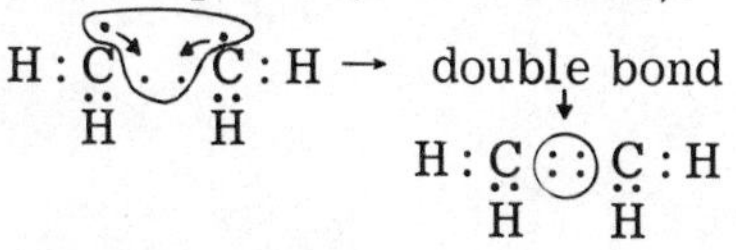

H : C̈ ⵈ C̈ : H → double bond

    Ḧ Ḧ

       H : C (⠶) C : H

         Ḧ Ḧ

On the following diagram, circle the *four* electrons which could form a double bond.

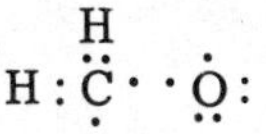

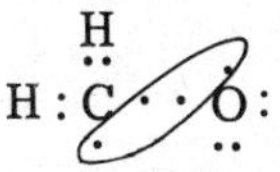

    H

H : C̈ ·· Ö :

   ·

    H

H : C̈ ·· Ö :

---

26. Circle the electrons involved in double bonds.

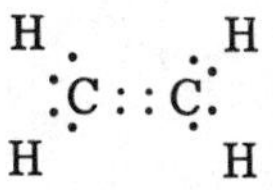

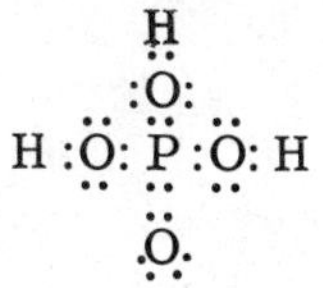

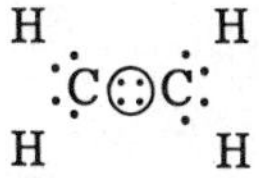

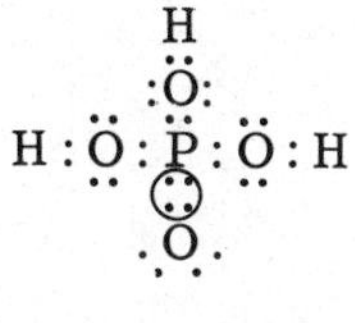

H .   . H

 :C :: C:

H .   . H

        H

       :Ö:

   H :Ö: P :Ö: H

       :Ö.

H   H

:C ⊙ C:

H   H

        H

      :Ö:

  H :Ö: P :Ö: H

       (⊙)

      .Ö.

---

27. How many electrons are in the outer shell of each atom?

H_____

O_____

P_____

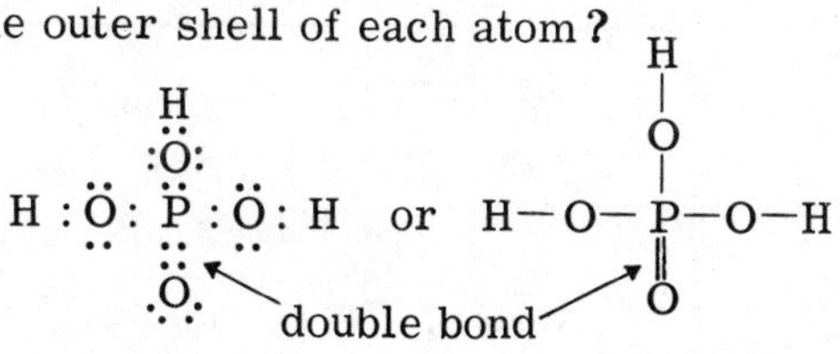

         H   H

       :Ö: O

H :Ö: P :Ö: H or H—O—P—O—H

       .Ö.   O

         double bond

(*Note* in Table A.2 that the second and third shell can sometimes contain a maximum of 10 electrons.)

Electrons: H____2____   C____8____   P____10____

28. In how many *bonds* (—) is *each* atom involved?

Each H_____

O_____

P_____

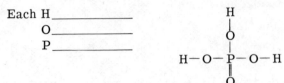

Note: A double bond counts as 2 covalent bonds.

H____1_____   Remember: P can form 5 bonds.

O____2_____

P____5_____

---

29. Complete the structural formula in the right-hand molecule.

H   H   H

C=C   O

H   H   H   O   P   O   H

O

H
|
O
|
H—O—P—O—H
‖
O

---

30. Write the structural formula for formaldehyde (CH_2O). Again, begin with the C, work to the right.

(If you miss this, copy the correct answer.)

31. Number of bonds?

Each H_____
O_____
C_____

$$\begin{array}{c} H \\ \diagdown \\ \diagup \\ H \end{array} C = O$$

- -

H_____1_____
O_____2_____
C_____4_____

_____

32. Is this structure possible?

$$\begin{array}{ccc} H & H \\ | & | \\ H-C-C-H \\ | & | \\ O & O-H \\ | & | \\ H & H \end{array}$$

Explain your answer.

- -

No
$$\begin{array}{ccc} H & H \\ | & | \\ H-C-C-H \\ | & | \\ O & \textcircled{O}-H \\ | & | \\ H & H \end{array}$$

This O has 3 covalent bonds. O can form only 2 covalent bonds.

_____

33. Write the structural formula for formic acid (HCO_2H).

- -

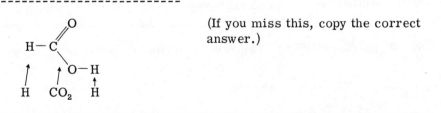

(If you miss this, copy the correct answer.)

34. Write the structural formula for acetic acid (CH_3CO_2H).

$$H-\underset{\underset{H}{|}}{\overset{\overset{H}{|}}{C}}-C\underset{O-H}{\overset{O}{\diagdown}}$$

---

35. What are the three fundamental particles of which atoms are composed?

Protons, neutrons, electrons (in any order)

---

36. In a calcium atom, what is the number of protons? _____
                                                electrons? _____

----

protons _____20_____
electrons _____20_____

---

37. How many electrons are in each shell of a calcium atom?

shell 1 _____   shell 2 _____
shell 3 _____   shell 4 _____

----

shell 1 _____2_____   shell 2 _____8_____
shell 3 _____8_____   shell 4 _____2_____

---

38. Write the outer shell diagram for a calcium atom.

· Ca ·

---

39. Define a covalent bond.

A *covalent bond* is formed by a *shared pair of electrons* (between atoms). (or similar response)

---

40. How many covalent bonds can each of the following form?

   H_____   C_____   O_____   P_____   S_____   N_____

   H___1___   C___4___   O___2___   P___5___   S___2___   N___3___

---

41. Diagram the structural formula for ethyl alcohol (CH_3CH_2OH).

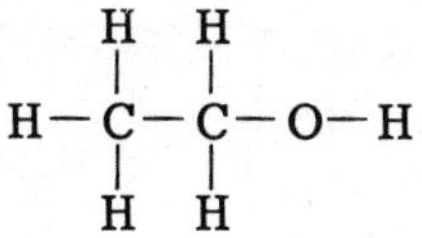

```
    H   H
    |   |
H — C — C — O — H
    |   |
    H   H
```

---

42. Diagram the structural formula for formaldehyde (CH_2O)

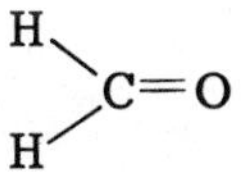

```
H
 \
  C = O
 /
H
```

---

43. Diagram the structural formula for carbon dioxide (CO_2).

- -

$O = C = O$

---

44. Diagram the structural formula for glycine ($CH_2NH_2CO_2H$).

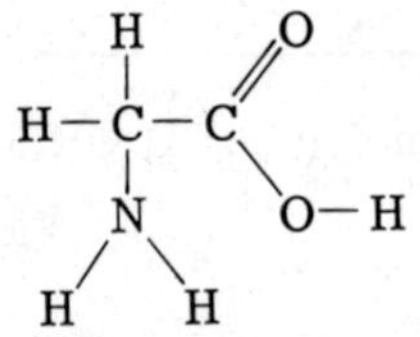

- -

(or similar response)

Take at least a 5-minute "break" before continuing on to the next unit.

UNIT *2* CHEMICAL GROUPS

Several specific groupings of atoms are common in biological chemistry. For example: fats contain long hydrocarbon chains; methyl and ethyl groups are constituents of many biological molecules; alcohols (OH groups) are common in carbohydrates and amino acids; the aldehyde configuration occurs in many carbohydrates; the carboxyl group is biochemically significant in carbohydrates, proteins, and nucleic acids; amino groups occur in proteins and nucleic acids; phosphate groups are constituents of nucleic acids, many carbohydrates and lipids in physiological systems; phosphate groups also function in energy transfer reactions; ester linkages join molecules in forming fats, nucleic acids, and many other larger compounds; and many biologically active molecules contain the benzene ring characteristic of a large number of aromatic compounds. Each of these groups will be encountered and used in later units of this book. Since they are used so frequently, an early acquaintance with them is desirable. Thus, you will learn to identify and diagram each of these submolecular groups of atoms.

Material Covered

> Hydrocarbons — Methyl and Ethyl groups
> Alcohols
> Aldehydes
> Organic acids — Carboxyl group
> Keto group
> Amino group
> Phosphate group
> Ester linkage
> Aromatic group

1. Which of the following molecules would you guess to be hydrocarbons (*hydrogen-carbon*)?

A.
$$
\begin{array}{c}
\quad\;\; H \quad H \\
\quad\;\; | \quad\;\; | \\
H-C-C-H \\
\quad\;\; | \quad\;\; | \\
\quad\;\; H \quad H
\end{array}
$$

D.
$$
\begin{array}{c}
\quad\;\; H \quad H \quad H \quad H \\
\quad\;\; | \quad\;\; | \quad\;\; | \quad\;\; | \\
H-C-C-C-C-H \\
\quad\;\; | \quad\;\; | \quad\;\; | \quad\;\; | \\
\quad\;\; H \quad H \quad H \quad H
\end{array}
$$

B.
$$
\begin{array}{c}
\quad\;\; H \quad O \quad\quad H \\
\quad\;\; | \quad\;\; \| \quad\quad / \\
H-C-C-N \\
\quad\;\; | \quad\quad\quad\;\; \backslash \\
\quad\;\; H \quad\quad\quad\; H
\end{array}
$$

E.
$$
\begin{array}{c}
\quad\;\; H \quad\quad\quad\;\; H \\
\quad\;\; | \quad\quad\quad\;\; | \\
H-C-C=C-C-H \\
\quad\;\; | \quad\;\; | \quad\;\; | \quad\;\; | \\
\quad\;\; H \quad H \quad H \quad H
\end{array}
$$

C.
$$
\begin{array}{c}
\quad\quad\quad H \\
\quad\quad\quad | \\
\quad\quad\quad O \\
\quad\quad\quad | \\
H-O-P=O \\
\quad\quad\quad | \\
\quad\quad\quad O-H
\end{array}
$$

- -

A, D, and E

---

2. What are the distinguishing characteristics of hydrocarbons?

- -

Hydrocarbons contain only *hydrogen* and *carbon* atoms. (or
similar response)

3.

$$CH_3 = H-\underset{\underset{H}{|}}{\overset{\overset{H}{|}}{C}}- \ = \text{Methyl group} \qquad C_2H_5 = H-\underset{\underset{H}{|}}{\overset{\overset{H}{|}}{C}}-\underset{\underset{H}{|}}{\overset{\overset{H}{|}}{C}}- \ = \text{Ethyl group}$$

Circle and label the methyl and ethyl groups in the following structural formulae.

$$H-\underset{\underset{H}{|}}{\overset{\overset{H}{|}}{C}}-OH \qquad H-\underset{\underset{H}{|}}{\overset{\overset{H}{|}}{C}}-N\overset{H}{\underset{H}{<}} \qquad H-\underset{\underset{H}{|}}{\overset{\overset{H}{|}}{C}}-\underset{\underset{H}{|}}{\overset{\overset{H}{|}}{C}}-O-\underset{\underset{H}{|}}{\overset{\overset{H}{|}}{C}}-H$$

- -

Methyl   Methyl   Ethyl   Methyl

---

4. <u>Alcohols</u>   <u>Non-Alcohols</u>

$$H-\underset{\underset{H}{|}}{\overset{\overset{H}{|}}{C}}-O-H \qquad\qquad H-\underset{\underset{H}{|}}{\overset{\overset{H}{|}}{C}}-\underset{\underset{O}{|}}{\overset{\overset{H}{|}}{C}}-\underset{\underset{H}{|}}{\overset{\overset{H}{|}}{C}}-H \qquad\qquad H-\underset{\underset{H}{|}}{\overset{\overset{H}{|}}{C}}-\underset{\underset{H}{|}}{\overset{\overset{H}{|}}{C}}-H$$

$$H-\underset{\underset{H}{|}}{\overset{\overset{H}{|}}{C}}-\underset{\underset{H}{|}}{\overset{\overset{H}{|}}{C}}-H \qquad\qquad\qquad H-\underset{\underset{H}{|}}{\overset{\overset{H}{|}}{C}}-O-\underset{\underset{H}{|}}{\overset{\overset{H}{|}}{C}}-H$$

$$H-\underset{\underset{H}{|}}{\overset{\overset{H}{|}}{C}}-N\overset{H}{\underset{H}{<}}$$

Is this an alcohol?

$$H-\underset{\underset{H}{|}}{\overset{\overset{H}{|}}{C}}-\underset{\underset{H}{|}}{\overset{\overset{H}{|}}{C}}-\underset{\underset{H}{|}}{\overset{\overset{H}{|}}{C}}-\underset{\underset{H}{|}}{\overset{\overset{H}{|}}{C}}-\underset{\underset{H}{|}}{\overset{\overset{H}{|}}{C}}-O-H$$

- -

Yes. [It contains a *hydroxyl* (—OH) group]

5. What is the distinguishing characteristic of the alcohols?

- -

All alcohols contain one or more —O—H (groups).
(—O—H = —OH = an OH group = a *hydroxyl group*.)

6. Which of the following are alcohols? (—O—H = —OH)

A. $\underset{\displaystyle H}{\overset{\displaystyle H}{H-\underset{|}{\overset{|}{C}}-OH}}$

B. $\underset{\displaystyle H}{\overset{\displaystyle H}{H-\underset{|}{\overset{|}{C}}-O-H}}$

C. $\underset{\displaystyle H}{\overset{\displaystyle H}{H-\underset{|}{\overset{|}{C}}-O-}}\underset{\displaystyle H\ H}{\overset{\displaystyle H\ H}{\underset{|}{\overset{|}{C}}-\underset{|}{\overset{|}{C}}-H}}$

D. $\underset{\displaystyle H\ \ \ H}{\overset{\displaystyle H\ H\ H}{H-\underset{|}{\overset{|}{C}}-\underset{|}{\overset{|}{C}}-\underset{|}{\overset{|}{C}}-H}}$
$$\underset{\displaystyle OH}{H-\underset{|}{\overset{|}{C}}-H}$$

E. $\underset{\displaystyle H\ H}{\overset{\displaystyle H\ H}{H-\underset{|}{\overset{|}{C}}-\underset{|}{\overset{|}{C}}-N}}\overset{\displaystyle H}{\underset{\displaystyle H}{}}$

F. CH_3OH

G. $CH_3CH_2NH_2$

H. $CH_3OCH_2CH_3$

- -

A, B, D, and F

7.   Aldehydes   Non-Aldehydes

$$H-C\underset{H}{\overset{O}{\diagup}}$$

$$H-\underset{H}{\overset{H}{\underset{|}{C}}}-C\underset{H}{\overset{O}{\diagup}}$$

$$H-\underset{OH}{\overset{H}{\underset{|}{C}}}-\underset{OH}{\overset{H}{\underset{|}{C}}}-C\underset{H}{\overset{O}{\diagup}}$$

$$H-\underset{H}{\overset{H}{\underset{|}{C}}}-\underset{H}{\overset{H}{\underset{|}{C}}}-OH$$

$$H-\underset{H}{\overset{H}{\underset{|}{C}}}-O-\underset{H}{\overset{H}{\underset{|}{C}}}-H$$

$$H-\underset{H}{\overset{H}{\underset{|}{C}}}-\overset{O}{\underset{}{\overset{\|}{C}}}-\underset{H}{\overset{H}{\underset{|}{C}}}-H$$

$$H-C\underset{OH}{\overset{O}{\diagup}}$$

Is this an aldehyde?

$$H-\underset{H}{\overset{H}{\underset{|}{C}}}-\underset{H}{\overset{H}{\underset{|}{C}}}-C\underset{H}{\overset{O}{\diagup}}$$

- -

Yes

_____

8. What are the distinguishing characteristics of an aldehyde?

- -

The $-C\underset{H}{\overset{O}{\diagup}}$ group.

_____

9. Which of the following are aldehydes?

A. $H-\underset{\underset{H}{|}}{\overset{\overset{H}{|}}{C}}-C\overset{\displaystyle O}{\underset{\displaystyle OH}{<}}$ D. $H-\underset{\underset{H}{|}}{\overset{\overset{H}{|}}{C}}-\overset{\displaystyle O}{\overset{\|}{C}}-\underset{\underset{H}{|}}{\overset{\overset{H}{|}}{C}}-H$

B. $H-C\overset{\displaystyle O}{\underset{\displaystyle H}{<}}$

E. $H-\underset{\underset{H}{|}}{\overset{\overset{H}{|}}{C}}-\underset{\underset{H}{|}}{\overset{\overset{H}{|}}{C}}-C\overset{\displaystyle O}{\underset{\displaystyle H}{<}}$

C. $H-\underset{\underset{H}{|}}{\overset{\overset{H}{|}}{C}}-O-\underset{\underset{H}{|}}{\overset{\overset{H}{|}}{C}}-\underset{\underset{H}{|}}{\overset{\overset{H}{|}}{C}}-H$

- -

B and E

---

10. Organic Acids   Non-Organic Acids

$H-C\overset{\displaystyle O}{\underset{\displaystyle OH}{<}}$

$H-\underset{\underset{H}{|}}{\overset{\overset{H}{|}}{C}}-OH$

$H-\underset{\underset{H}{|}}{\overset{\overset{H}{|}}{C}}-C\overset{\displaystyle O}{\underset{\displaystyle OH}{<}}$

$H-\underset{\underset{H}{|}}{\overset{\overset{H}{|}}{C}}-C\overset{\displaystyle O}{\underset{\displaystyle H}{<}}$

$H-\underset{\underset{H}{|}}{\overset{\overset{H}{|}}{C}}-C\overset{\displaystyle O}{\underset{\displaystyle OH}{<}}$
$\underset{HH}{\overset{N}{\diagup\diagdown}}$

$H-\underset{\underset{H}{|}}{\overset{\overset{H}{|}}{C}}-O-\underset{\underset{H}{|}}{\overset{\overset{H}{|}}{C}}-H$

Is this an organic acid?

$H-\underset{\underset{H}{|}}{\overset{\overset{H}{|}}{C}}-\underset{\underset{H}{|}}{\overset{\overset{\overset{\displaystyle HH}{\diagdown\diagup}}{N}}{|}}{C}-C\overset{\displaystyle O}{\underset{\displaystyle OH}{<}}$

- -

Yes

---

11. Write the group that is characteristic of an organic acid.

     This is also called a *carboxyl* group.

----

12. Circle and label each group you recognize on the following
molecules.

$$
\begin{array}{ccc}
\text{H} & \text{H} & \\
| & | & \diagup\text{O} \\
\text{H}-\text{C}-\text{C}-\text{C} & & \\
| & | & \diagdown\text{OH} \\
\text{H} & \text{H} &
\end{array}
\qquad
\begin{array}{c}
\text{H} \\
| \\
\text{H}-\text{C}-\text{O}-\text{H} \\
| \\
\text{H}
\end{array}
\qquad
\begin{array}{cc}
\text{H} & \\
| & \diagup\text{O} \\
\text{H}-\text{C}-\text{C} & \\
| & \diagdown\text{H} \\
\text{H} &
\end{array}
$$

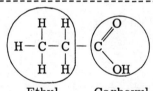 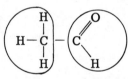

Ethyl   Carboxyl   Methyl Hydroxyl   Methyl   Aldehyde
           (acid)   (alcohol)

13. Write the structural formula for each of the following groups.

Hydroxyl (alcohol)

Aldehyde

Carboxyl

Methyl

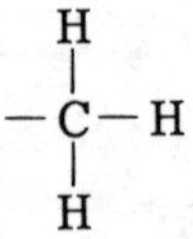

Ethyl

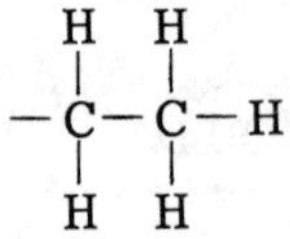

Hydroxyl $-OH$

Aldehyde $-C\overset{\displaystyle O}{\underset{\displaystyle H}{}}$

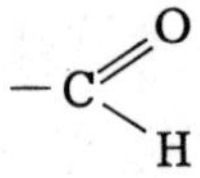

Carboxyl $-C\overset{\displaystyle O}{\underset{\displaystyle OH}{}}$

Methyl $-\overset{\displaystyle H}{\underset{\displaystyle H}{C}}-H$

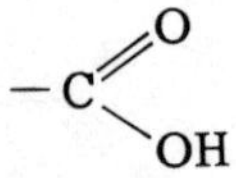

Ethyl $-\overset{\displaystyle H\ \ H}{\underset{\displaystyle H\ \ H}{C-C}}-H$

---

14. Are all molecules which contain $-OH$ groups alcohols?

No   (The carboxyl group $-C\overset{\displaystyle O}{\underset{\displaystyle OH}{}}$ contains an OH group, but is characteristic of organic acids.)

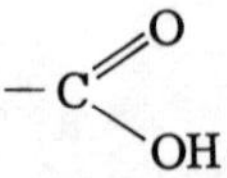

15. <u>Contain a keto group</u>   <u>Do not contain a keto group</u>

$$H-\overset{\overset{\displaystyle H}{|}}{\underset{\underset{\displaystyle H}{|}}{C}}-\overset{\overset{\displaystyle O}{\|}}{C}-\overset{\overset{\displaystyle H}{|}}{\underset{\underset{\displaystyle H}{|}}{C}}-H$$

$$H-\overset{\overset{\displaystyle H}{|}}{\underset{\underset{\displaystyle H}{|}}{C}}-O-\overset{\overset{\displaystyle H}{|}}{\underset{\underset{\displaystyle H}{|}}{C}}-H$$

$$H-\overset{\overset{\displaystyle H}{|}}{\underset{\underset{\displaystyle OH}{|}}{C}}-\overset{\overset{\displaystyle O}{\|}}{C}-\overset{\overset{\displaystyle H}{|}}{\underset{\underset{\displaystyle H}{|}}{C}}-OH$$

$$H-\overset{\overset{\displaystyle H}{|}}{\underset{\underset{\displaystyle H}{|}}{C}}-C\overset{\displaystyle O}{\diagdown}_{H}$$

$$H-\overset{\overset{\displaystyle H}{|}}{\underset{\underset{\displaystyle H}{|}}{C}}-C\overset{\displaystyle O}{\diagdown}_{OH}$$

Does this molecule contain a keto group?

$$H-\overset{\overset{\displaystyle H}{|}}{\underset{\underset{\displaystyle H}{|}}{C}}-O-\overset{\overset{\displaystyle H}{|}}{\underset{\underset{\displaystyle H}{|}}{C}}-\overset{\overset{\displaystyle H}{|}}{\underset{\underset{\displaystyle H}{|}}{C}}-H$$

- -

No.

---

16. What are the characteristics of a keto group?

- -

$$-C-\overset{\overset{\displaystyle O}{\|}}{C}-C- \qquad \left(not\ -C\overset{\displaystyle O}{\diagdown}_{H} \quad or \quad -C\overset{\displaystyle O}{\diagdown}_{OH} \right)$$

Note that the $\overset{\overset{\displaystyle O}{\|}}{C}$ is attached to two other carbon atoms.

---

17. Which of the following contain a keto group?

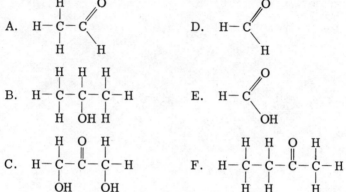

C and F

18. Contain amino groups   Do not contain amino groups

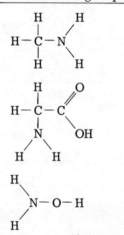

S=C=C=S

$$H-\underset{\underset{H}{|}}{\overset{\overset{H}{|}}{C}}-C=N-OH$$

Does the following contain an amino group?

$$H-\underset{\underset{H}{|}}{\overset{\overset{H}{|}}{C}}-\underset{\underset{H}{|}}{\overset{\overset{H}{|}}{C}}-N\overset{\diagup H}{\diagdown H}$$

Yes

19. Write the structural formula for an amino group.

- -

$$-N\begin{array}{c} H \\ \\ H \end{array}$$

20.

$$-O-\overset{\overset{\displaystyle O}{\|}}{\underset{\underset{\displaystyle OH}{|}}{P}}-OH \quad \text{is a phosphate group.}$$

Circle the phosphate group in the following molecule:

$$H-\overset{\overset{\displaystyle H}{|}}{\underset{\underset{\displaystyle H}{|}}{C}}-\overset{\overset{\displaystyle O}{\|}}{C}-O-\overset{\overset{\displaystyle O}{\|}}{\underset{\underset{\displaystyle OH}{|}}{P}}-OH$$

- -

$$H-\overset{\overset{\displaystyle H}{|}}{\underset{\underset{\displaystyle H}{|}}{C}}-\overset{\overset{\displaystyle O}{\|}}{C}-\boxed{O-\overset{\overset{\displaystyle O}{\|}}{\underset{\underset{\displaystyle OH}{|}}{P}}-OH}$$

---

21. Write the structural formula for a phosphate group.

- -

$$-O-\overset{\overset{\displaystyle O}{\|}}{\underset{\underset{\displaystyle OH}{|}}{P}}-OH$$

22. Circle and label each group you recognize in the following molecules.

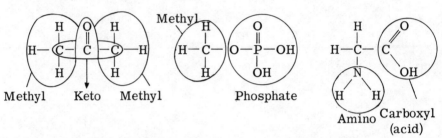

---

23. Write the structural formula for each of the following:

Phosphate

Keto

Amino

Phosphate $-O-\overset{\overset{O}{\|}}{\underset{\underset{OH}{|}}{P}}-OH$

Keto $C-\overset{\overset{O}{\|}}{C}-C$

Amino $-N\overset{\diagup H}{\diagdown H}$

24. A carboxyl group and a hydroxyl group can combine in an *ester* linkage with the loss of H_2O.

$$\text{For example, } H-\underset{\underset{H}{|}}{\overset{\overset{H}{|}}{C}}-O-H \qquad \overset{O}{\underset{H-O}{\diagdown}}C-\underset{\underset{H}{|}}{\overset{\overset{H}{|}}{C}}-H$$

Methyl alcohol   Acetic acid

Circle the H_2O atoms which could be split out as an ester linkage is formed (if you are confused, guess). Diagram the structural formula of methyl acetate (the molecule that contains the ester linkage). Circle the ester linkage.

- -

$$H-\underset{\underset{H}{|}}{\overset{\overset{H}{|}}{C}}-\boxed{OH} \qquad \overset{O}{\underset{\boxed{H}-O}{\diagdown}}C-\underset{\underset{H}{|}}{\overset{\overset{H}{|}}{C}}-H \quad \text{or} \quad H-\underset{\underset{H}{|}}{\overset{\overset{H}{|}}{C}}-O-\boxed{H} \qquad \overset{O}{\underset{\boxed{H-O}}{\diagdown}}C-\underset{\underset{H}{|}}{\overset{\overset{H}{|}}{C}}-H$$

$$H-\underset{\underset{H}{|}}{\overset{\overset{H}{|}}{C}}-\boxed{O-\overset{O}{\overset{\|}{C}}}-\underset{\underset{H}{|}}{\overset{\overset{H}{|}}{C}}-H$$

_____

25. Draw the structural formula for methyl formate. ($HCOOCH_3$)

- -

$$H-\overset{\overset{O}{\|}}{C}-O-\underset{\underset{H}{|}}{\overset{\overset{H}{|}}{C}}-H$$

_____

26. Which of the following are esters?

A.
$$H-\overset{\overset{\displaystyle H}{|}}{\underset{\underset{\displaystyle H}{|}}{C}}-O-\overset{\overset{\displaystyle O}{\parallel}}{C}-H$$

C.
$$H-\overset{\overset{\displaystyle H}{|}}{\underset{\underset{\displaystyle H}{|}}{C}}-\overset{\overset{\displaystyle O}{\parallel}}{C}-\overset{\overset{\displaystyle H}{|}}{\underset{\underset{\displaystyle H}{|}}{C}}-H$$

B.
$$H-\overset{\overset{\displaystyle H}{|}}{\underset{\underset{\displaystyle H}{|}}{C}}-O-\overset{\overset{\displaystyle H}{|}}{\underset{\underset{\displaystyle H}{|}}{C}}-H$$

D.
$$H-\overset{\overset{\displaystyle O}{\parallel}}{C}-O-\overset{\overset{\displaystyle H}{|}}{\underset{\underset{\displaystyle H}{|}}{C}}-H$$

- -

A and D

---

27.   Aromatic   Non-Aromatic

Is this molecule an aromatic compound?

- -

Yes

28. What structure is characteristic of an aromatic compound?

- -

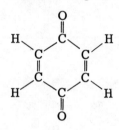

---

29. The structure you just diagrammed is a benzene ring. Is this a benzene ring?

- -

No

---

30. Without consulting preceding items, write a benzene (aromatic) ring.

- -

or

31.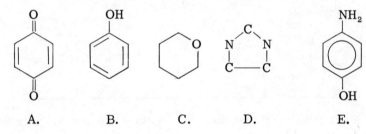

Which of the following are aromatic compounds?

A.   B.   C.   D.   E.

- -

B and E

---

32. Group review: Match the following:

Alcohol _____

Aldehyde _____

Amino _____

Aromatic _____

Carboxyl _____

Ester linkage _____

Ethyl _____

Keto _____

Methyl _____

Phosphate _____

A. $H-\underset{\underset{H}{|}}{\overset{\overset{H}{|}}{C}}-\underset{\underset{H}{|}}{\overset{\overset{H}{|}}{C}}-$

B. $-OH$

C. $-O-\underset{\underset{OH}{|}}{\overset{\overset{O}{\|}}{P}}-OH$

D. $-N\overset{\diagup H}{\diagdown H}$

E. $-C\overset{\diagup O}{\diagdown OH}$

F. $-\underset{\underset{H}{|}}{\overset{\overset{H}{|}}{C}}-H$

G. $-C\overset{\diagup O}{\diagdown H}$

H. $-C-\overset{\overset{O}{\|}}{C}-C-$

I. $-\overset{\overset{O}{\|}}{C}-O$

J.

- -

Alcohol	B	Carboxyl	E	Keto	H
Aldehyde	G	Ester linkage	I	Methyl	F
Amino	D	Ethyl	A	Phosphate	C
Aromatic	J				

33. Label all the groups you know in the following molecules.

```
      H  H                      H  O      O                    H       O
      |  |                      |  ||     ||                   |      //
  H—C—C—OH                  H—C—C—O—P—OH               H—C—C
      |  |                      |         |                    |       \
      H  H                      H         OH                   N        OH
                                                              / \
                                                             H   H
```

- - - - - - - - - - - - - - - - - - - -

| Ethyl | Hydroxyl (alcohol) | Methyl | Ester linkage | Phosphate | | Amino | Acid or Carboxyl |

34. Diagram each of the following groups.

Ethyl

Amino

Phosphate

- -

Ethyl
```
         H  H
         |  |
      —C—C—H
         |  |
         H  H
```

Amino
```
              H
             /
      —N
             \
              H
```

Phosphate
```
              O
              ||
      —O—P—OH
              |
              OH
```

35. Diagram each of the following groups.

   Keto

   Aromatic

   Carboxyl (acid)

   Ester linkage

Keto $-C-\overset{\overset{O}{\|}}{C}-C-$

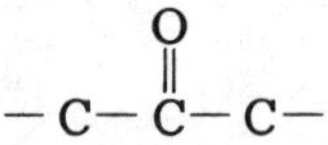

Aromatic   (see diagram)   or   (benzene ring)   or   (benzene ring)

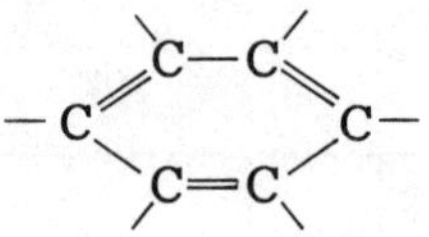

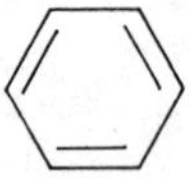

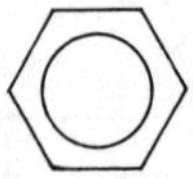

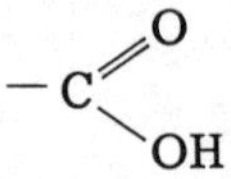

Carboxyl $-C\overset{O}{\underset{OH}{\big\langle}}$

Ester linkage $-C\overset{O}{\underset{O-}{\big\langle}}$

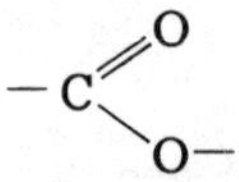

36. Diagram each of the following groups:

       Methyl   Hydroxyl (alcohol)   Aldehyde

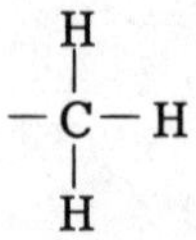

$-\overset{\overset{\displaystyle H}{|}}{\underset{\underset{\displaystyle H}{|}}{C}}-H$ $-O-H$ $-C\overset{O}{\underset{H}{\big\langle}}$

      Methyl   Alcohol   Aldehyde

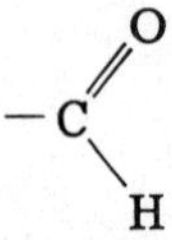

Take at least a 5-minute break before continuing on to the next unit.

UNIT *3* *IONS, SALTS, CRYSTALS*

In the first two units the bonds you have dealt with have been co-valent bonds. Several other types of bonding, or mutual attraction between atoms, are significant in biological systems. This unit introduces ionic bonding, which is due to the attraction between atoms or groups of opposite charge (+ and −). Ionic bonding occurs in crystal structure and salts. Ions are produced when salts dissolve in water and are major constituents of all living things. This unit will give you a background for understanding ionic bonding and ions. The significance of charged atoms and groups (ions) in biochemistry will be introduced later in this program.

Material Covered

Ions
Ionic bond
Salts
Dissociation of salts

---

1. What electrostatic charge (+ or −) do you associate with electrons? _____ protons? _____ Which of the following electrostatic charge pairs are attracted to one another? (+ +) (+ −) (− −)?

- -

   electrons_____ − _____ protons _____ + _____
   (+ −) (Opposite charges attract; like charges repel.)

---

2. A covalent bond is due to electrostatic attraction. For example, in water H $:\overset{..}{\text{O}}:$ H, what part of the hydrogen atom (nucleus or electron) is attracted to the oxygen nucleus?

- -

   Electron (The − electron is attracted to the + oxygen nucleus. Thus, the H atom is bonded to the O atom by the electrostatic attraction between its electron and the + oxygen nucleus.)

---

3. In a water molecule, to what molecular component is the hydrogen nucleus attracted?

- -

The electrons (the + hydrogen nucleus is attracted to the − electrons)

4. List the following for a sodium atom.

Number of protons_____.
Number of electrons_____.

Is the sodium atom electrostatically neutral; (the total + charge of the nucleus equals the total − charge of the electrons) (protons equals electrons)?

- -

Number of protons_____11_____
Number of electrons_____11_____
Yes (+ = −)

5. In general, the outer shell of an *ion* is either empty or complete when compared to an atom.

Outer Shell Diagrams

Atoms	Ions	Ionic Charge
Na ·	Na	+1
· Ca ·	Ca	+2
: Cl .	: Cl :	−1
. Ö .	: Ö :	−2

Check the table carefully to determine the characteristics of ions. Is the following an ion? If so, what is its charge?

: F̈ :

- -

Yes
−1

6. What is the general characteristic of the ions in the preceding item (when compared to the atoms)?

The ions have gained or lost electrons and bear a charge. (or similar response)

---

7. The sodium ion is written Na^+. Ca ion $= Ca^{++}$.

   Write the symbol for the Mg ion.
   Write the symbol for the K ion.

   Mg^{++} and K^+

---

8. Outer Shell Diagram

   $: \overset{..}{\underset{..}{Cl}} .$

How many electrons can Cl accept to form an ion (complete the outer electron shell)? Write the symbol for the Cl ion.

   One
   Cl^-

---

9. Write the symbol for each of the following ions:

   Na_____   Mg_____   K _____
   Cl _____   Ca _____   F _____

| Na | Na^+ | Mg | Mg^{++} | K | K^+ |
| Cl | Cl^- | Ca | Ca^{++} | F | F^- |

10. Cation = $\oplus$ ion   Pronounced: CAT' ION
Anion = $\ominus$ ion

Pronounce cation and anion out loud three times each.

Label each as a cation or anion.

| Na_____ | Mg_____ | K _____ |
| Cl_____ | Ca _____ | F _____ |

- -

| Na | cation | Mg | cation | K | cation |
| Cl | anion | Ca | cation | F | anion |

---

11. A *salt* is a general term for an *ionic* compound. Of what units is a salt composed?

- -

Ions

---

12. Most salts have metallic (e.g., sodium, potassium, magnesium, iron, calcium) cations. Circle the metallic ion in each of these salts.

$Na^{\oplus}Cl^{\ominus}$ $Ca^{++}F_2^{\ominus}$ $Fe^{++}Cl_2^{\ominus}$

- -

$\boxed{Na^{\oplus}}Cl^{\ominus}$ $\boxed{Ca^{\oplus\oplus}}F_2^{\ominus}$ $\boxed{Fe^{++}}\,Cl_2^{\ominus}$

---

13. How would you define a salt?

- -

A salt is composed of ions; the cation is usually a metallic ion. (or similar response)

---

14. For convenience, an ionic bond is usually diagrammed to indicate the attraction of opposite charges. Thus, sodium formate could be written:

formate ion → (H—C with =O and O$^\ominus$) Na$^\oplus$ when formic acid is H—C with =O and O—H .

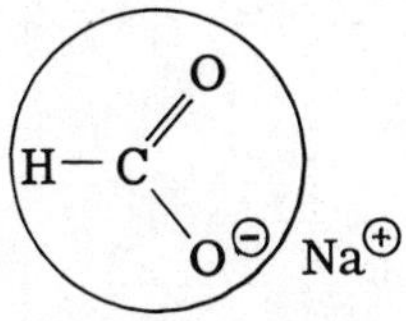

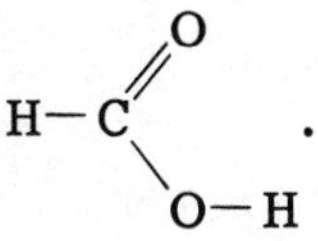

Write the **structural** formula for sodium acetate when acetic acid

is H—C(H)(H)—C with =O and O—H . Circle the acetate ion.

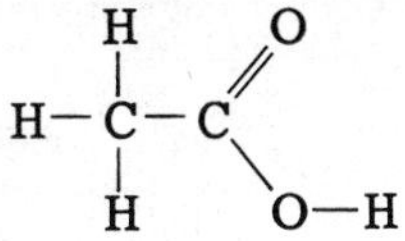

- -

(H—C(H)(H)—C with =O and O$^\ominus$) Na$^\oplus$

_____

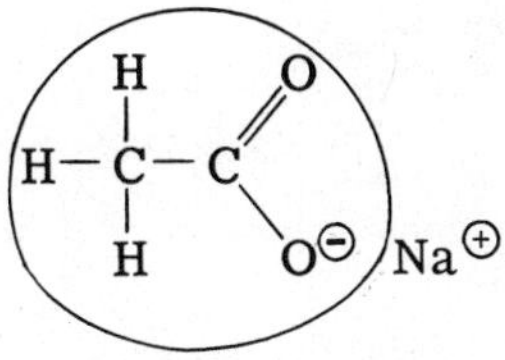

15. Even though sodium acetate is written H—C(H)(H)—C with =O and O$^\ominus$Na$^\oplus$, it is

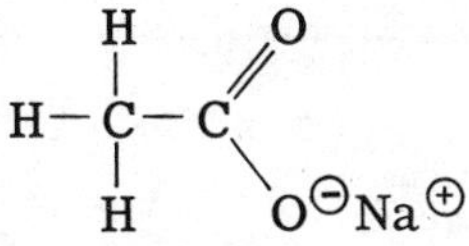

also a crystalline or an ionic compound. What is the negative ion (ionic group) in this organic salt (Na acetate)?

- -

Acetate ion   (H—C(H)(H)—C with =O and O$^\ominus$)

_____

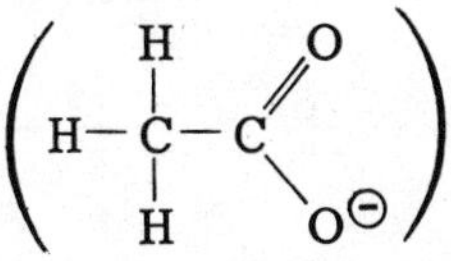

16. How many electrons are in the outer shell of the "lower oxygen" $(-O^\ominus)$ of the acetate ion?

----

8      $\left(-C\overset{\displaystyle \nearrow^{O}}{\underset{:\ddot{O}:^\ominus}{}} \right)$

---

17. Organic salts are named in the same fashion as organic acids and aldehydes:

Aldehyde	Acid	Salt or Ion
Form/aldehyde	Form/ic Acid	Form/ate
Acetaldehyde	?	?

Fill in the (?) in the table. What ending is characteristic of an organic acid? What ending is characteristic of an organic salt or ion?

Acetic acid, acetate
-ic (acid)
-ate (salt)

---

18. Label each of the following as salt or acid:

      Lactic_____
      Fumarate_____
      Propionic_____
      Succinate_____
      Pyruvate_____

      Lactic_____acid_____
      Fumarate_____salt_____
      Propionic_____acid_____
      Succinate_____salt_____
      Pyruvate_____salt_____

19. What ions are produced when sodium formate $\left(H-C\begin{subarray}{l} \diagup\diagup O \\ \diagdown O^{\ominus}Na^{\oplus} \end{subarray} \right)$ dissociates (forms ions)? Label the cation and the anion.

$Na^{\oplus}$ and   formate$^{\ominus}$ $\left(H-C\begin{subarray}{l} \diagup\diagup O \\ \diagdown O^{\ominus} \end{subarray} \right)$

(cation)   (anion)

---

20. What ions are formed when $H-\overset{\displaystyle H}{\underset{\displaystyle H}{C}}-C\begin{subarray}{l} \diagup\diagup O \\ \diagdown O^{\ominus}\ Na^{\oplus} \end{subarray}$ dissociates?

$H-\overset{\displaystyle H}{\underset{\displaystyle H}{C}}-C\begin{subarray}{l} \diagup\diagup O \\ \diagdown O^{\ominus} \end{subarray}$ $+ Na^{\oplus}$

(acetate)

---

21. Most salt crystals are very soluble in water. When a salt dissolves, it dissociates into ions. What ions are produced when KCl dissociates in water?

K^{+} and Cl^{-}

22. Dissociation can also be written as an equation:

$$K^{\oplus}Cl^{\ominus} + H_2O \rightleftharpoons K^{\oplus}(aq) + Cl^{\ominus}(aq)$$ (aq) indicates an aqueous medium.

The double arrow $\rightleftharpoons$ indicates that the dissociation is reversible (i.e., $K^{\oplus}$ and $Cl^{\ominus}$ can combine to form $K^{\oplus}Cl^{\ominus}$). Write the equation for the dissociation of $Na^{\oplus}F^{\ominus}$ in water.

- -

$$Na^{\oplus}F^{\ominus} + H_2O \rightleftharpoons Na^{\oplus}(aq) + F^{\ominus}(aq)$$

23. Write the equation for the dissociation of $Ca^{\oplus\oplus}Cl_2^{\ominus}$.

- -

$$Ca^{\oplus\oplus}Cl_2^{\ominus} + H_2O \rightleftharpoons Ca^{\oplus\oplus}(aq) + 2Cl^{\ominus}(aq)$$

24. $Na^{\oplus}F^{\ominus} + H_2O \rightleftharpoons Na^{\oplus}(aq) + F^{\ominus}(aq)$

For each $Na^{\oplus}F^{\ominus}$, how many + charges are produced?
                     how many − charges are produced?
                     does the total + = the total − ?

- -

one
one
yes

25. $Ca^{\oplus\oplus}Cl_2^{\ominus} + H_2O \rightleftharpoons Ca^{\oplus\oplus}(aq) + 2Cl^{\ominus}(aq)$

Total + charges produced?_____
Total − charges produced?_____
Are they equal?_____

- -

2
2
yes

26. State a generalization about the relationship between the + and
    − charges on the ions which are produced when a salt dissociates.

----

   total + = total − (or similar response)

---

27. Would the following make sense? Explain your answer.
    $$Mg^{++}Cl_2^{-} + H_2O \rightleftharpoons Mg^{++}(aq) + Cl^{-}(aq)$$

----

   no
   total + = 2
   total − = 1   They should be equal.

---

28. All chemical bonding is due to what forces?

   Electrostatic attraction; attraction between + and − charges. (or
   similar response)

---

29. In ionic compounds, what units are held together by electrostatic
    attraction?

   Ions (+ and −).

Take at least a 5-minute "break" before continuing.

UNIT 4 BONDS — HYDROGEN, DIPOLAR, HYDROPHOBIC

In addition to covalent and ionic bonding, three other types of bonds are of sufficient importance to receive attention here: dipole-dipole bonds, hydrogen bonds, and hydrophobic bonds. The hydrogen bond is a type of dipole-dipole bond which is of special significance in protein structure, nucleic acid structure, and enzyme function. Hydrogen bonding is also involved in the solubility of materials in water. Hydrophobic bonding is a relatively new concept which is now recognized as being of great importance in biological membrane structure and function, protein structure, and enzyme action. A thorough grasp of the nature of these types of bonding will enable you to understand the interactions between large molecules later on.

Material Covered

  Dipoles
  Hydrogen bond
  Dipole — Dipole bond
  Polar groups
  Solubility (based on polar groups and H bonding)
  Non-polar groups
  Hydrophobic bonds
  General definition of a bond

---

1. A hydrogen atom is composed of a single proton and a single electron. In the equation

    $$H^{\oplus}Cl^{\ominus} + H_2O \rightleftharpoons H^{\oplus}(aq) + Cl^{\ominus}(aq),$$

    what happens to the H's electron? What is a H^+ (hydrogen ion) in terms of protons and electrons?

- -

  The electron is attached to the Cl^- (or similar answer).
  $H^{\oplus}$ = a proton (Actually the H^+ attracts water so strongly that it never occurs "naked" in aqueous medium.)

---

2. The pair of electrons shared between some nuclei are unequally shared.

    Example, in H_2O: H : Ö: H

    The electrons are held more closely to the O than to the H.

    Each H in this diagram is a single proton. What charge (+ or −) would be associated with each H?

  +

---

3. Detailed experimental analysis of water molecules reveals that the two H atoms tend to be located on one side of the O thus:

    H   H   (not H—O—H)   H   Remember the charges:
      O   :Ö: H   electron (−)

      structural formula   outer shell   proton (+)
                           diagram

    Label the areas of this water molecule in which the protons predominate and the area in which the electrons predominate.

    H   H
      O

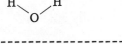 Protons predominate
              Electrons predominate

---

4. Label one atom (end) of this water molecule (δ^-) and *two* atoms (ends) (δ^+).

    H   H
      O

    (δ^+ or δ^-, the Greek delta symbol, is used to indicate a fractional charge which is smaller than a full unit of ionic charge)

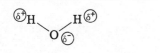

---

5. Any molecule with + and − ends is called a *dipole* (two poles).

   + and − (electrostatic attraction)
   (− and −) or (+ and +) (electrostatic repulsion)

   Arrange these dipoles in a line with their ends touching.

   -

   | + | | + | | + | | or | | + | | + | | + |

6. Water is actually a tripole: $^{\ominus}$H $_{\diagdown}$H $^{\oplus}$
                                            O $_{\ominus}$

   Draw two molecules of water with *one* H of one molecule attracted
   to the O of the other molecule.

   -

   H$_{\diagdown}$ $_{\diagup}$H
          O

      H$_{\diagdown}$ $_{\diagup}$H   (or other reasonable arrangement)
             O

7. Each O^{-} can attract *two* H^{+} from *different* H_2O molecules. Arrange
   three water molecules to show this:

   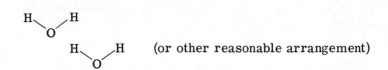

   -

       H$_{\diagdown}$ $_{\diagup}$H
              O
   H$_{\diagdown}$ $_{\diagup}$H H$_{\diagdown}$ $_{\diagup}$H   (or other reasonable arrangement)
          O   O

8. The attraction of an H atom in a dipole for a negative atom in another dipole (e.g., O in water) is called a *hydrogen bond*.

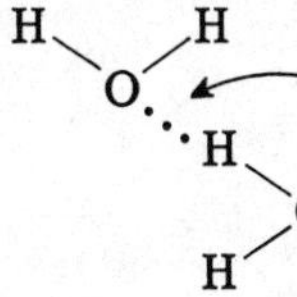

H H
O — Hydrogen bond (···)
H
O
H

The $=O$ in a carboxyl group $\left(-C\begin{smallmatrix}O\\OH\end{smallmatrix}\right)$ is also a (δ^-) atom.

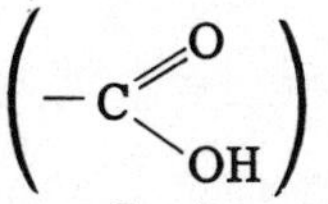

Diagram a H bond between the $=O$ of a carboxyl group and a water molecule.

- -

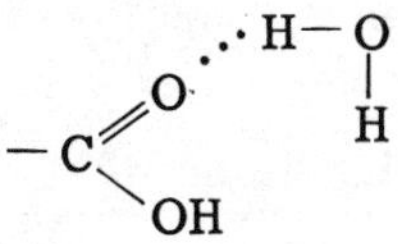

H — O
O H
— C
OH

9. Diagram a H bond between the $=O$ of a carboxyl group and an H in an amino group $\left(-N\begin{smallmatrix}H\\H\end{smallmatrix}\right)$.

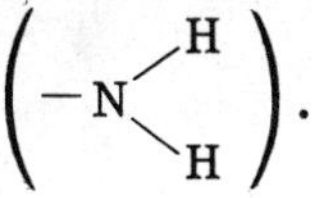

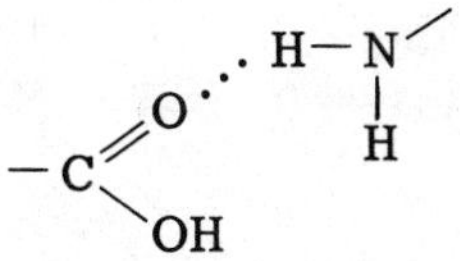

- -

H — N
O H
— C
OH   (or similar diagram)

10. In the following structure, the right-hand N is a (δ^-) atom. Diagram a H bond with a molecule of water.

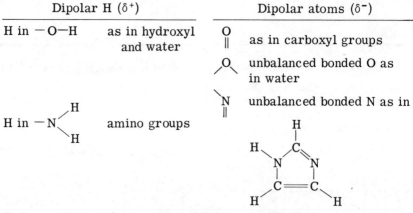

---

11. The following atoms are of particular importance in biological H bonding:

Dipolar H (δ^+)		Dipolar atoms (δ^-)	
H in $-O-H$	as in hydroxyl and water	$\overset{O}{\underset{\parallel}{}}$	as in carboxyl groups
		$\overset{O}{\diagup\diagdown}$	unbalanced bonded O as in water
H in $-N\overset{H}{\underset{H}{\diagdown}}$	amino groups	$\overset{\diagdown}{\underset{\parallel}{N}}$	unbalanced bonded N as in

Define a H bond (you may use the above material).

A H bond is the electrostatic attraction between a (+) dipolar H atom which is covalently bonded to an O or N atom and a (−) dipolar atom, such as an O or N. (or similar response)

12. Using the concepts you have learned, write a general definition for any dipole-dipole bond.

- -

A dipole-dipole bond is the attraction between the + end of one dipole and the − end of another dipole. (or similar response)

---

13. You have already learned that these groups are polar (charged).

Label the appropriate atoms with a charge (δ^+ or δ^-)

- -

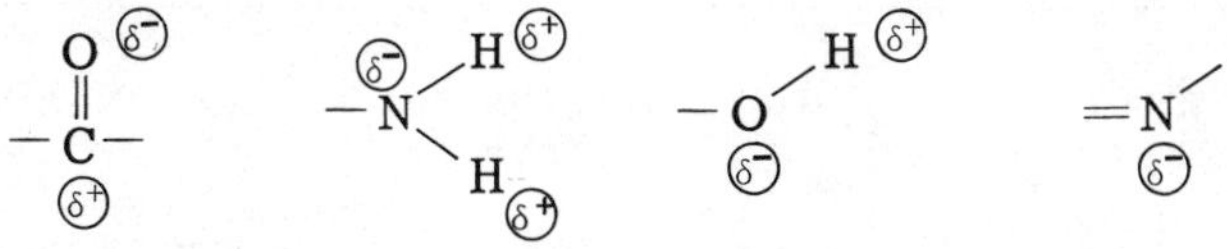

---

14. All —OH groups contain an unbalanced bonded $O\left(-O^{\diagup H}\right)$. Rewrite the following molecules with OH groups to show this. Add the δ^+ and δ^- to all the polar atoms.

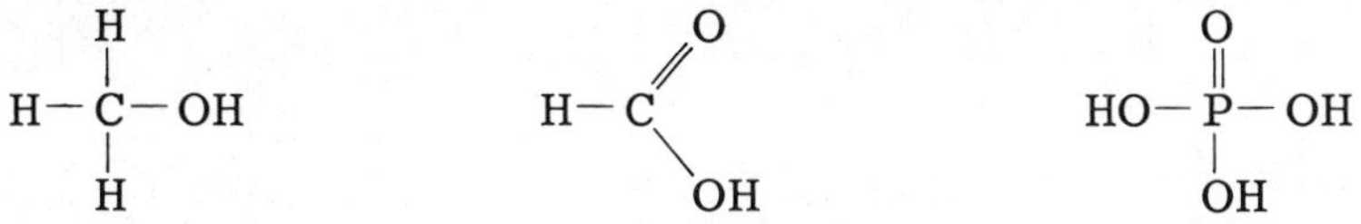

- -

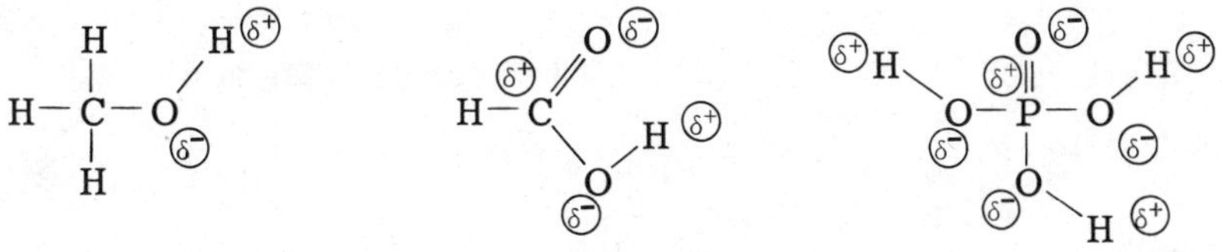

---

15. Diagram the attraction of two water molecules to this molecule of formaldehyde:

$$\text{H}\diagdown \atop \text{H}\diagup \text{C}\mathord=\text{O}$$

- -

$$\begin{array}{c} \text{H}-\text{O} \diagdown \\ \qquad \text{H} \\ \qquad \vdots \\ \text{H}-\text{C} \mathord= \text{O}\cdots\text{H} \diagdown \\ \qquad | \qquad \qquad \text{O} \\ \qquad \text{H} \qquad \text{H} \diagup \end{array}$$ (or similar diagram)

---

16. Diagram the attraction of water molecules to this molecule of methyl alcohol.

$$\begin{array}{c} \qquad \text{H} \\ \qquad | \\ \text{H}-\text{C}-\text{O} \\ \qquad | \quad | \\ \qquad \text{H} \ \ \text{H} \end{array}$$

- -

$$\begin{array}{c} \quad \text{O} \\ \text{H} \diagup \ \diagdown \text{H} \qquad \qquad \text{H} \\ \ \ \text{H} \ \ \vdots \qquad \qquad | \\ \text{H}-\text{C}-\text{O}\cdots\text{H}-\text{O} \\ \quad | \qquad \diagdown \text{H} \\ \quad \text{H} \qquad \quad \vdots \\ \qquad \qquad \qquad \text{O} \\ \qquad \quad \text{H} \diagup \ \diagdown \text{H} \end{array}$$ (or similar diagram)

---

17. H which is covalently bonded to C $\left(\ \begin{matrix} & H \\ & | \\ H-&C-H \\ & | \\ & H \end{matrix}\ \right)$ is *non-polar* (it

does not bear a charge) due to the equal nature of the electron

sharing. $\ \begin{matrix} H & H \\ | & | \\ H-C-&C- \\ | & | \\ H & H \end{matrix}$ is thus a non-polar group. It does not form

H bonds. Is $\ \begin{matrix} H & H & H \\ | & | & | \\ H-C-&C-&C- \\ | & | & | \\ H & H & H \end{matrix}$ a polar or non-polar group? Will

this group attract water molecules?

Non-polar
No

_____

18. Circle the non-polar groups. Write the appropriate charge on the atoms of polar groups.

$\ \begin{matrix} H & & H \\ | & & \diagup \\ H-C-&O & \\ | & & \\ H & & \end{matrix}$ $\ \begin{matrix} H & H & H & & O \\ | & | & | & & \diagup\!\!\diagup \\ H-C-&C-&C-&C & \diagdown \ H \\ | & | & | & & O \diagup \\ H & H & H & & \end{matrix}$

----

19. The solubility of a molecule in water is determined by its ability
    to attract water (form H bonds with water). Will polar groups in-
    crease or decrease solubility? Will non-polar groups increase
    or decrease solubility?

    Increase
    Decrease

20. On the following molecules, circle the groups which will increase
    the solubility of the molecule.

21. Ions are atoms or groups which bear a + or − charge. Would an
    ion be soluble in water? Explain your response briefly using a
    diagram.

    Yes
    Ions (+ or −) would attract water molecules. E.g., a + ion would
    attract water thus:

22. What type of group is insoluble? What two types of groups or atoms are soluble?

Insoluble — non-polar groups
Soluble — ions and polar groups

---

23. Non-polar groups are also called *hydrophobic groups* (water-fearing groups). Hydrocarbons are the most common hydrophobic groups in biological material. Circle and label the hydrophobic groups.

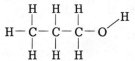

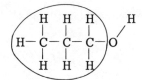   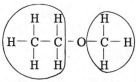

hydrophobic group (propyl)   hydrophobic group (ethyl)

hydrophobic
group
(methyl)

---

24. In an aqueous medium (i.e., in water), polar groups and ions will be surrounded by molecules of _____. Hydrophobic groups will tend to cluster together (e.g., "oil and water do not mix"). On these molecules, circle the groups which will be surrounded by water molecules and label them "H_2O," also circle the hydrophobic groups and connect these circles with a line to indicate clustering.

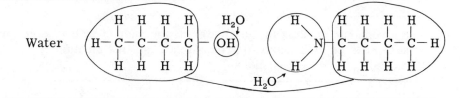

25. The clustering together of hydrophobic groups is called *hydro-phobic bonding*, which occurs in water. The tendency toward hydro-phobic bonding increases with the increase in length of the hydro-carbon chain. Which of the following would have the greatest tendency to form hydrophobic bonds?

A.
$$
\begin{array}{ccccc}
H & H & H & H & H \\
| & | & | & | & | \\
-C- & C- & C- & C- & C-H \\
| & | & | & | & | \\
H & H & H & H & H
\end{array}
$$

C.
$$
\begin{array}{c}
H \\
| \\
-C-H \\
| \\
H
\end{array}
$$

B.
$$
\begin{array}{cc}
H & H \\
| & | \\
-C- & C-H \\
| & | \\
H & H
\end{array}
$$

D.
$$
\begin{array}{cccc}
H & H & H & H \\
| & | & | & | \\
-C- & C- & C- & C-H \\
| & | & | & | \\
H & H & H & H
\end{array}
$$

A

----

26. Which of the following groups would form hydrophobic bonds?

A. $-OH$ C. $-NH_2$

B.
$$
\begin{array}{ccc}
H & H & H \\
| & | & | \\
-C- & C- & C-H \\
| & | & | \\
H & H & H
\end{array}
$$

D. $-C\begin{array}{c} {}^{\nearrow O} \\ {}_{\searrow OH} \end{array}$

E. $-C\begin{array}{c} {}^{\nearrow O} \\ {}_{\searrow O^{\ominus}Na^{\oplus}} \end{array}$

F.
$$
\begin{array}{cc}
H & H \\
| & | \\
-C- & C-H \\
| & | \\
H & H
\end{array}
$$

B and F

----

27. As you may have guessed, the preceding account of hydrophobic bonding is rather naive and oversimplified. A more adequate ex-planation is based on energetic and thermodynamic principles that we will not take time to develop. Thus, define hydrophobic bonding as well as you can at this time.

Hydrophobic bonding is the clustering together of hydrophobic (or non-polar or hydrocarbon) groups in an aqueous medium (in water). (or similar response)

----

28. In a covalent bond, two atoms are held together by common attraction for a pair of electrons. In an ionic bond, 2 ions are held
together by electrostatic attraction (+ and −). In a dipolar bond,
2 dipoles are held together by electrostatic attraction. In a hydrogen bond, a H atom is held to a ⑥⁻ atom by electrostatic attraction.
In your own words, what is the general definition of a bond?

A bond is any force which holds two atoms together. (or any
similar response)

29. Label with the appropriate dipolar charges (δ^+ or δ^-).

30. Rediagram these molecules to illustrate hydrogen bonding between
the =O and one H of the NH_2.

31. On the diagram, circle the groups or portions of the molecule which will *retard* water solubility.

- -

(may be included)

----

32. What is hydrophobic bonding?

- -

Hydrophobic bonding is the clustering together of hydrophobic groups in an aqueous medium. (or similar response)

Take at least a 5-minute break before continuing to the next unit.

UNIT 5 EQUILIBRIUM

Chemical equilibrium is an essential concept for understanding biological chemistry. Here, you will learn some rudiments of what makes a reaction "go." The relationships between the concentrations of the reactants and the equilibrium will be covered as a basis for following chemical reaction sequences from living systems. If you can do the last item in this sequence correctly, you should have a foundation for tracing biochemical pathways.

Material Covered

Reactants and products of a reaction
Reaction rate as a function of concentration
Equilibrium
Effect of changes in concentration on rate and concentration

---

1. $A + B \rightleftharpoons C + D$
   This reversible reaction is made up of a *forward reaction* and a *reverse reaction*. Write and label the forward and reverse reactions.

   Forward: $A + B \rightarrow C + D$
   Reverse: $A + B \leftarrow C + D$ (or $C + D \rightarrow A + B$)
   (All biochemical reactions are theoretically reversible.)

---

2. $A + B \rightleftharpoons C + D$
   Consider the *reverse* reaction only.
   What are the *products* of the reverse reaction? What are the *reactants* of the reverse reaction?

   Products — A and B
   Reactants — C and D

---

3. The *relative rates* of the forward and reverse reactions may be represented by adding an arrow above or below the reaction arrows. In the following, is the rate greatest for the forward or reverse reaction?
   A. $CO_2 + H_2O \rightleftharpoons H_2CO_3$
   B. $Q + R \rightleftharpoons S + T$
   C. $ATP + H_2O \rightleftharpoons ADP + P$
   D. $A + B \rightleftharpoons C + D$

   A. Reverse
   B. Forward
   C. Forward
   D. Equal

---

4. This reaction is in *equilibrium.* At chemical equilibrium what is the relationship between the rates of the forward and reverse reactions?
   $A + B \rightleftharpoons C + D$

   The forward rate equals the reverse rate.

---

5. Which of the following reactions are in equilibrium?
   A. $A + B \rightleftharpoons C + D$
   B. $A + B \rightleftharpoons C + D$
   C. $ATP + H_2O \rightleftharpoons ADP + P$
   D. $CO_2 + H_2O \rightleftharpoons H_2CO_3$
   E. $ADP + P \rightleftharpoons ATP + H_2O$

   A, C, and E (any order)

---

6. Define chemical equilibrium.

   Chemical equilibrium for a reversible reaction exists when the rate of the forward reaction equals the rate of the reverse reaction. (or similar response)

7. $A + B \rightleftharpoons C + D$

   For which reaction (forward or reverse) is the rate the greatest?
   Is the concentration of each of the following increasing or decreasing?

   A_____ B_____ C_____ D_____

   ----

   forward
   A_decreasing_ B_decreasing_ C_increasing_ D_increasing_

8. LeChatelier's principle states that if a system at equilibrium is
   stressed, it will respond to *relieve* the stress and to obtain a new
   equilibrium.

   $A + B \rightleftharpoons C + D$

   This reaction starts at equilibrium. "A" is added to the system.
   What effect does this have on the concentration of "A"? This is
   a stress. Will an increase in the rate of the forward or reverse
   reaction relieve this stress? What happens to the concentration
   of "A" as the stress is relieved?

   Increased.
   Forward reaction
   The concentration of A will decrease (the decrease in the concen-
   tration of A *is* the relief of the stress).

   Pronunciation: LeChatelier
      LOO (as in look) SHAH – TELL – YAY'

9. Indicate the response of this reaction to the stress by drawing a
   "relative rate arrow."

   $A + B \rightleftharpoons C + D$ The concentration of D is increased (D is added).

   $A + B \rightleftharpoons C + D$

10. State LeChatelier's principle.

If a chemical system is stressed, it will react to relieve the
stress and to attain a new equilibrium. (or similar response)

---

11. In the reaction $A + B \rightleftharpoons C + D$, if the concentration of A is increased, which reaction rate is increased? What are the products
of the forward reaction? What are the reactants of the forward
reaction?

Forward
Products — $C + D$
Reactants — $A + B$

---

12. The *rate* of a reaction *depends on* the concentration of the *reactants only*.
$$A + B \rightleftharpoons C + D$$
The concentration of A is decreased. For which reaction is A a
reactant? Thus, in which reaction will the rate be affected? Will
this rate be decreased or increased? Which reaction rate is now
greater? Indicate this (the relative rates) by adding a "relative
rate arrow."

Forward
Forward
Decreased
Reverse
$A + B \rightleftharpoons C + D$

---

13. $A + B \rightleftharpoons C + D$
The concentration of C is decreased. Add a "relative rate arrow"
to indicate the response to this stress.

$A + B \rightleftharpoons C + D$

14. Add a "relative rate arrow" for each of the following stresses:

Stress	Reaction: $A + B \rightleftharpoons C + D$

A. C increased
B. B increased
C. C decreased
D. D decreased
E. A and B increased

A. ←   C. →   E. →
B. →   D. →

---

15. $A + B \rightleftharpoons C + D$
Is this reaction at equilibrium? Is the concentration of A increasing or decreasing? Is the concentration of C increasing or decreasing?

No
A is decreasing.
C is increasing.

---

16. $A + B \rightleftharpoons C + D$
The concentration of A is increased. Add a "relative rate arrow."
What is the effect of this increase in the concentration of A on the concentration of:

C_____   D_____   B_____

→   C increases   D increases   B decreases
(These changes continue until a new equilibrium is attained.)

---

17. $Q + R \rightleftharpoons S + T$
The concentration of S is decreased. Add a "relative rate arrow."
What is the effect on the concentration of:

T_____   Q_____   R_____

→   T increases   Q decreases   R decreases

18. In this reaction which occurs in mammalian muscle cells during exercise:

   pyruvate + 2 DPNH $\rightleftharpoons$ lactate + 2 DPN

   What effect would an increase in DPNH concentration have on the reaction rate? What effect would an increase in DPNH concentration have on lactate concentration?

Rate of forward reaction increased ($\rightarrow$).
Lactate concentration increased.

---

19. $CO_2 + H_2O \rightleftharpoons H_2CO_3 \rightleftharpoons H^+ + HCO_3^-$

   This reaction occurs in the blood. In the lungs CO_2 (carbon dioxide) leaves the blood. What effect would this decrease in CO_2 concentration have on the H^+ concentration of the blood?

H^+ will decrease. ($CO_2 + H_2O \rightleftharpoons H_2CO_3 \rightleftharpoons H^+ + HCO_3^-$)

Take at least a 5-minute break before continuing on to the next unit.

REVIEW – UNITS 1-5

Retention of material you have learned is a vexing educational problem! This review covers the main points of the first five units and will help you to check your level of retention. Work through it just as you have the preceding units. Whenever you judge your response to be inadequate, however, check back over the items indicated in the response space. Review carefully to be certain you understand the principles involved. If you wish, you may go over this review unit again later to check your retention and to drill the major points covered thus far. The review units should communicate to you the level of expectation for retention and should help you to know at what level subsequent material should be learned.

---

1. For calcium (atomic number = 20) fill in each of the following numbers:
   Protons in nucleus
   Electrons in shell No. 1
   Electrons in shell No. 2
   Electrons in shell No. 3
   Electrons in shell No. 4

----

  20   No. 1 — 2   No. 2 — 8   No. 3 — 8   No. 4 — 2
                              (*If you miss this, review Unit 1, Items 1-8*)

---

2. Write the *outer shell diagram* for fluorine (atomic number = 9)

$:\overset{..}{\underset{..}{F}}\cdot$ (*If you miss this, review Unit 1, Items 9-12*)

---

3. How many covalent bonds can each of the following atoms form?

C_____   O_____   H_____   N_____   S_____

C___4___   O___2___   H___1___   N___3___   S___2___

Review: Unit 1, Items 13-24

4. Write the structural formula for pyruvic acid (CH_3COCO_2H).

$$H-\overset{\overset{\displaystyle H}{|}}{\underset{\underset{\displaystyle H}{|}}{C}}-\overset{\overset{\displaystyle O}{\|}}{C}-\overset{\overset{\displaystyle O}{\diagup}}{C}_{\diagdown OH}$$

(If you miss this, review Unit 1, Items 24-40)

5. Group review: match the following:

Alcohol_____
Aldehyde_____
Amino_____
Aromatic_____
Carboxyl_____
Ester linkage_____
Ethyl_____
Keto_____
Methyl_____
Phosphate_____

A. $H-\overset{\overset{\displaystyle H}{|}}{\underset{\underset{\displaystyle H}{|}}{C}}-\overset{\overset{\displaystyle H}{|}}{\underset{\underset{\displaystyle H}{|}}{C}}-$

B. $-OH$

C. $-O-\overset{\overset{\displaystyle O}{\|}}{\underset{\underset{\displaystyle OH}{|}}{P}}-OH$

D. $-N\overset{\diagup H}{\diagdown H}$

E. $-C\overset{\diagup\diagup O}{\diagdown OH}$

F. $-\overset{\overset{\displaystyle H}{|}}{\underset{\underset{\displaystyle H}{|}}{C}}-H$

G. $-C\overset{\diagup\diagup O}{\diagdown H}$

H. $-\overset{\overset{\displaystyle O}{\|}}{C}-C-C-$

I. $-\overset{\overset{\displaystyle O}{\|}}{C}-O-$

J. $\bigcirc$

Alcohol	B	Ester linkage	I
Aldehyde	G	Ethyl	A
Amino	D	Keto	H
Aromatic	J	Methyl	F
Carboxyl	E	Phosphate	C

Review: Unit 2, appropriate sections

6. Diagram each of the following groups:

Ethyl

Amino

Phosphate

- -

Ethyl

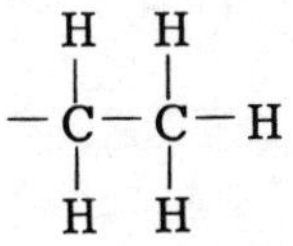

$$
\begin{array}{cc}
H & H \\
| & | \\
-C-C-H \\
| & | \\
H & H
\end{array}
$$

Review: Unit 2, Items 1-3

Amino

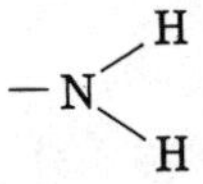

$$
-N\!\!\begin{array}{c} {}^{H} \\ {}_{H} \end{array}
$$

Review: Unit 2, Items 18-19

Phosphate

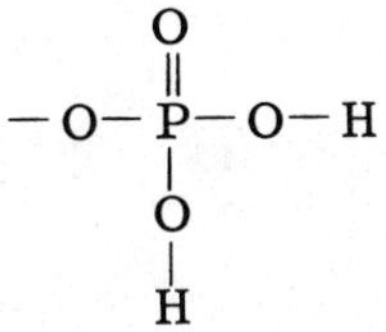

$$
\begin{array}{c}
O \\
\| \\
-O-P-O-H \\
| \\
O \\
| \\
H
\end{array}
$$

Review Unit 2, Items 20-21

7. Diagram each of the following groups:

    Keto

    Aromatic

    Carboxyl (acid)

    Ester linkage

Keto $-C-\overset{\overset{\displaystyle O}{\|}}{C}-C-$ *Review: Unit 2, Items 15-17*

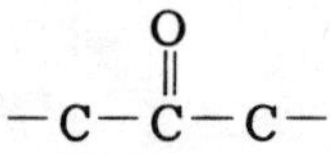

Aromatic   (six-membered ring)   or

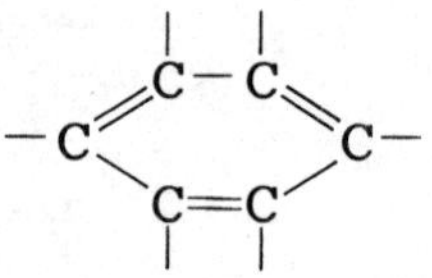

    (benzene ring)   or   (benzene ring)   *Review: Unit 2, Items 27-31*

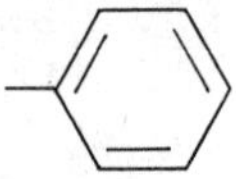

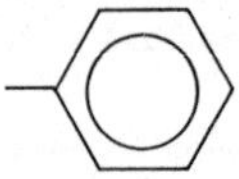

Carboxyl $-C\overset{\displaystyle O}{\underset{\displaystyle OH}{\big<}}$ *Review: Unit 2, Items 10 and 11*

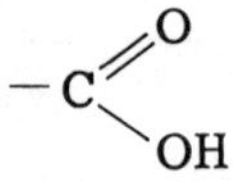

Ester linkage $-C\overset{\displaystyle O}{\underset{\displaystyle O-}{\big<}}$ *Review: Unit 2, Items 24-26*

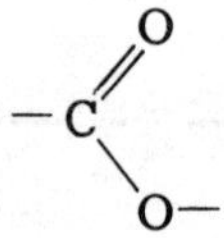

8. Diagram each of the following groups:

Methyl

Hydroxyl (alcohol)

Aldehyde

Methyl $-\overset{\displaystyle H}{\underset{\displaystyle H}{C}}-H$ *Review: Unit 2, Items 1-3*

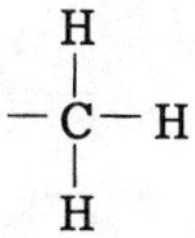

Alcohol $-O-H$ *Review: Unit 2, Items 4-6*

Aldehyde $-C\overset{\displaystyle O}{\underset{\displaystyle H}{<}}$ *Review: Unit 2, Items 7-9*

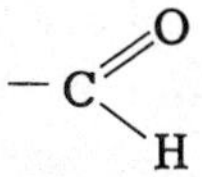

---

9. Write the symbol for each of the following ions:

Na_____		Ca_____	
Cl _____		K _____	
Mg_____		F _____	

- -

Na	Na^+	Ca	Ca^{++}
Cl	Cl^-	K	K^+
Mg	Mg^{++}	F	F^-

Review: Unit 3, Items 1-6

10. Write the equation for the dissociation of the organic salt, sodium acetate $(CH_3CO_2^{\ominus} Na^{\oplus})$.

$$
\begin{array}{ccc}
H & O & \\
| & \diagup\!\!\diagup & \\
H-C-C & & + H_2O \rightleftharpoons \\
| & \diagdown{}_{\ominus\ \oplus} & \\
H & ONa &
\end{array}
\quad
\begin{array}{cc}
H & O \\
| & \diagup\!\!\diagup \\
H-C-C & \quad (aq) + Na^{\oplus}(aq) \\
| & \diagdown{}_{\ominus} \\
H & O
\end{array}
$$

(If you miss this, review Unit 3, Items 7-26)

---

11. Diagram an H bond with the right-hand N and an H of an amino group.

$$
\begin{array}{c}
H \\
| \\
C \diagdown\!\!\diagdown \\
H-N \qquad N \\
| \qquad\quad | \\
H-C = C \\
\qquad | \\
\qquad H
\end{array}
$$

$$
\begin{array}{cc}
H & \qquad H \diagdown \\
| & \qquad\quad N- \\
C \diagdown\!\!\diagdown & \diagup \\
H-N \qquad N\cdots H & \\
| \qquad\quad | & \\
H-C = C & \diagdown\ (3\ dots) \\
\qquad | & \\
\qquad H &
\end{array}
$$

Review: Unit 4, Items 1-9

---

12. What is the major factor influencing the solubility of a chemical substance?

The capacity to form H bonds or ionic dipolar bonds with water. (or similar response)

Review: Unit 4, Items 10-22

ANSWER SHIELD

Use this slider to cover all frames below the one you are working.

Atomic Weights

Element	Atomic Number	Atomic Weight
Hydrogen	1	1.0
Helium	2	4.0
Lithium	3	6.9
Beryllium	4	9.0
Boron	5	10.8
Carbon	6	12.0
Nitrogen	7	14.0
Oxygen	8	16.0
Fluorine	9	19.0
Neon	10	20.1
Sodium	11	23.0
Magnesium	12	24.3
Aluminum	13	27.0
Silicon	14	28.1
Phosphorus	15	31.0
Sulfur	16	32.1
Chlorine	17	35.5
Argon	18	39.9
Potassium	19	39.1
Calcium	20	40.1

Two-Place Logarithms

Number	Logarithms
1	0.00
2	0.30
3	0.48
4	0.60
5	0.70
6	0.78
7	0.85
8	0.90
9	0.95

Table A.1

Atomic Name	Atomic Symbol	Atomic Number	Atomic Name	Atomic Symbol	Atomic Number
Argon	Ar	18	Lithium	Li	3
Beryllium	Be	4	Magnesium	Mg	12
Boron	B	5	Neon	Ne	10
Calcium	Ca	20	Nitrogen	N	7
Carbon	C	6	Oxygen	O	8
Chlorine	Cl	17	Phosphorus	P	15
Fluorine	F	9	Potassium	K	19
Helium	He	2	Sodium	Na	11
Hydrogen	H	1	Sulfur	S	16

Table A.2

Shell Number	Maximum Electrons per Shell
1	2
2	8(10)
3	8(10)
4	

Eight electrons is the usual maximum number;
10 is sometimes the maximum number.

13. What type of groups participate in hydrophobic bonding?

Hydrocarbon (or non-polar) groups.

Review: Unit 4, Items 16-25

---

14. Define chemical equilibrium.

For a reversible reaction, at equilibrium the rate of the forward reaction equals the rate of the reverse reaction. (or ⇀ = ↼).
(or similar response) *Review: Unit 5, Items 1-7*

---

15. In the reaction:

$$H-\underset{\underset{H}{|}}{\overset{\overset{H}{|}}{C}}-\underset{\underset{OH}{|}}{\overset{\overset{H}{|}}{C}}-C\overset{\displaystyle O}{\underset{\displaystyle OH}{\diagdown}} \rightleftharpoons H-\underset{\underset{H}{|}}{\overset{\overset{H}{|}}{C}}-\underset{}{\overset{\overset{\displaystyle O}{\|}}{C}}-C\overset{\displaystyle O}{\underset{\displaystyle OH}{\diagdown}} + 2H$$

Lactic acid   Pyruvic acid

If the concentration of pyruvic acid is decreased, what will be the effect on the concentration of lactic acid. Explain your response briefly.

Lactic acid concentration decreases. Explanation: ⇌; the rate of the reverse reaction is decreased. (or similar response)

Review: Unit 5, Items 8-19

Take at least a 5-minute break before continuing with the next unit.

UNIT 6 CARBOHYDRATES I

Carbohydrates, as sugars and starches, are the major class of foodstuffs for living organisms. The simple sugars, or monosaccharides, are the basic units from which the larger and more complex carbohydrates are constructed. You will learn the names and structural formulae for several of the common biologically important monosaccharides in this unit. We will not, however, attempt to demonstrate or learn any details of carbohydrate chemistry as it occurs in photosynthesis or respiration. When you study these complex reaction sequences they should be easier to follow and more meaningful if you remember the material from this unit and the next one.

Carbohydrates also function in biological systems as such structural molecules as cellulose in plant cell walls and as the intercellular "cement" which helps to hold animal cells together.

Material Covered

General formula of carbohydrates
Terminology of sugars
Pyruvic and lactic acids
Glucose
Shorthand structural formulae
Galactose
Fructose

---

1. Carbohydrates: Carbo + hydrate (carbon + water)
   Empirical formula: $C_n(H_2O)_n$
   A 3-carbon carbohydrate: $C_3H_6O_3$
   A 4-carbon carbohydrate: $C_4H_8O_4$
   What would be the empirical formula for a 5-carbon carbohydrate?

- -

$C_5H_{10}O_5$

---

2. Write the empirical formula for a 6-carbon carbohydrate.

$C_6H_{12}O_6$ Note: there are some exceptions to this general
               formula $C_n(H_2O)_n$

3. Sugars are carbohydrates.
Sugars: Glucose
         Ribose
         Fructose
What would you guess to be the name for malt sugar?

Maltose

4. What word ending is characteristic for sugars?

-ose

5. Complete the table:

Sugar	Number of Carbon Atoms	Greek or Latin Number
Triose	3	Treis
Tetrose	4	Tetra
	5	Penta
	6	Hex
	7	Hepta
	8	Octa

Pentose   Heptose
Hexose   Octose

6. How many carbons does a hexose have?

6

---

7. All the following are carbohydrates:

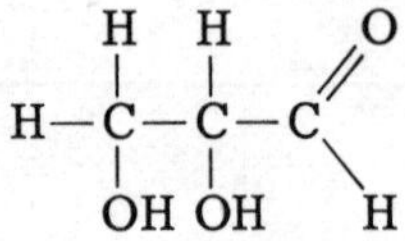

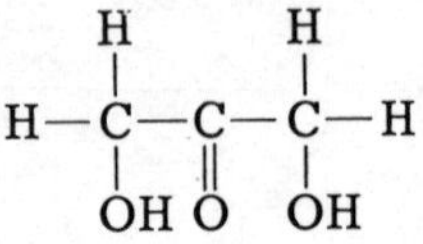

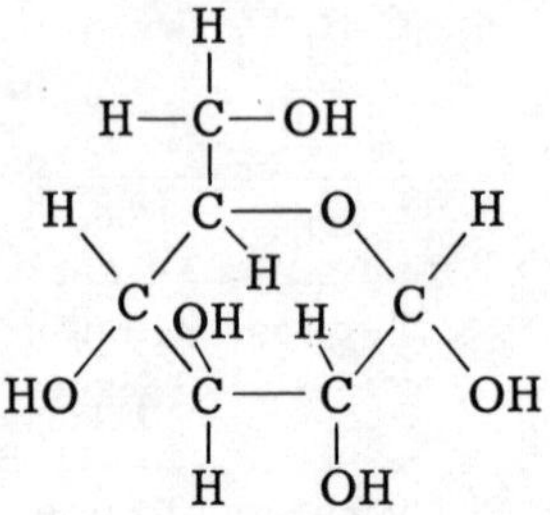

What chemical group (studied in Unit 2) is found in *all* carbohydrates? What other group is found in the first (at the left)? What other group is found in the second?

$-$ OH (hydroxyl)

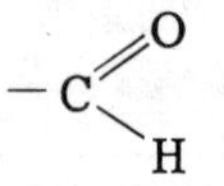

(aldehyde)

(keto)

8. Another definition of simple carbohydrates is that they are poly-
hydroxyaldehydes or polyhydroxyketones. Label each of these
correctly.

A.
$$
\begin{array}{c}
O \diagup\!\!\!\!\diagdown H \\
C \\
| \\
H-C-OH \\
| \\
H-C-OH \\
| \\
H
\end{array}
$$

B.
$$
\begin{array}{c}
H \\
| \\
H-C-OH \\
| \\
C=O \\
| \\
H-C-OH \\
| \\
H
\end{array}
$$

A. Polyhydroxyaldehyde
B. Polyhydroxyketone

9. Pyruvic acid and lactic acid are related to the trioses. *Pyruvic
acid* contains a keto group; *lactic acid* does not. Which two molecules below are acids? Which formula is pyruvic acid and which
is lactic acid?

A.
$$
\begin{array}{c}
H \\
| \\
H-C-OH \\
| \\
C=O \\
| \\
H-C-OH \\
| \\
H
\end{array}
$$

B.
$$
\begin{array}{c}
O \diagup\!\!\!\!\diagdown OH \\
C \\
| \\
C=O \\
| \\
H-C-H \\
| \\
H
\end{array}
$$

C.
$$
\begin{array}{c}
O \diagup\!\!\!\!\diagdown OH \\
C \\
| \\
H-C-OH \\
| \\
H-C-H \\
| \\
H
\end{array}
$$

D.
$$
\begin{array}{c}
O \diagup\!\!\!\!\diagdown H \\
C \\
| \\
H-C-OH \\
| \\
H-C-OH \\
| \\
H
\end{array}
$$

B and C
B. Pyruvic acid
C. Lactic acid

10. The formula for lactic acid is $CH_3CHOHCO_2H$ or $CH_3CHOHCOOH$. Write the structural formula.

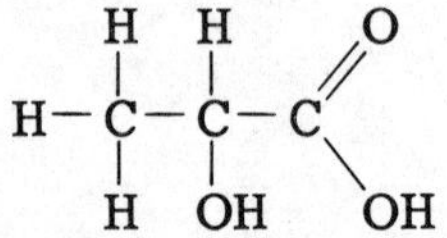

(Lactic acid is a product of glucose utilization in muscle during exercise; its accumulation is a causal factor in the development of fatigue.)

11. Write the structural formula for lactic acid without consulting the preceding items.

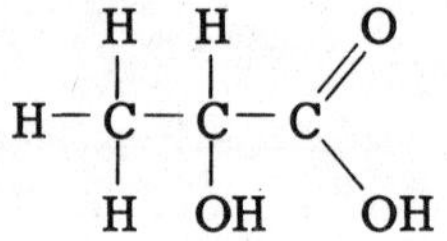

----

12. The formula for pyruvic acid is CH_3COCO_2H or $CH_3COCOOH$. Write the structural formula for pyruvic acid.

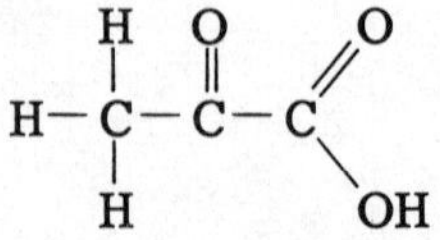

(Pyruvic acid is a three-carbon intermediate in the metabolic breakdown of glucose in almost all cells.)

13. Write the structural formula for pyruvic acid.

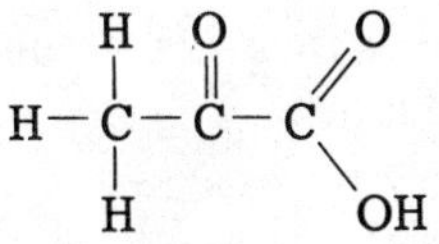

$$\text{H}-\overset{\overset{\displaystyle \text{H}}{|}}{\underset{\underset{\displaystyle \text{H}}{|}}{\text{C}}}-\overset{\overset{\displaystyle \text{O}}{\|}}{\text{C}}-\text{C}\begin{smallmatrix}\nearrow \text{O}\\ \searrow \text{OH}\end{smallmatrix}$$

----

14. A *monosaccharide* is a carbohydrate which cannot be broken down into smaller carbohydrates by treatment with acid. The most common monosaccharides are pentoses and hexoses.

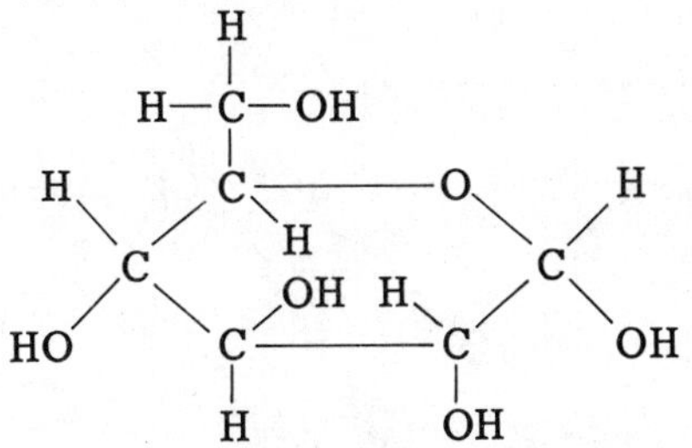

Glucose

Is glucose a hexose or a pentose? Does glucose conform to the general formula for carbohydrates $(C_n(H_2O)_n)$?

Hexose
Yes $(C_6H_{12}O_6)$
(Glucose is one of the fundamental foods — fuels — for the cells of higher organisms; both plants and animals.)

15. The carbons are numbered thus:

Without consulting the preceding diagram, copy this "skeleton" and try to complete the structural formula for glucose.

- -

Correct any errors you made. Note that the H and OH are inverted on carbon #3. (This is an oversimplification of the rather complex phenomenon of stereoisomerism.)

16. Write the structural formula for glucose.

- -

$$
\begin{array}{c}
\text{H} \\
| \\
\text{H}-\text{C}-\text{OH}
\end{array}
$$

17. Which carbon (by number) is not in the glucose "ring"?

- -

#<u>6</u>

18. The glucose ring is usually written in "shorthand" form:

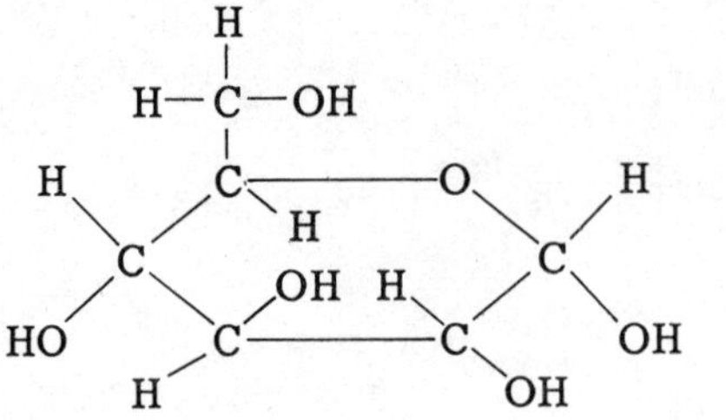

or

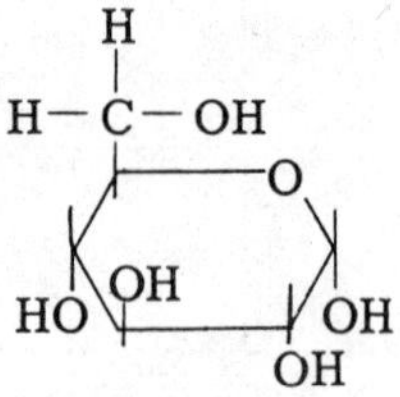

or

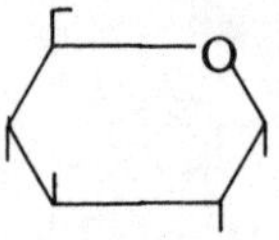

In the lower diagram, what does the (Γ) represent?
In the lower diagram, what does the (|) represent?

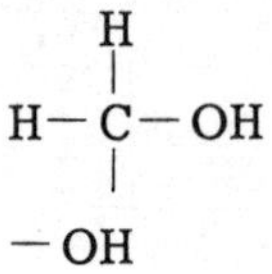

- -

or CH_2OH

$-OH$

---

19. Complete this skeleton by adding OH groups and a CH_2OH group to make a "shorthand" glucose formula.

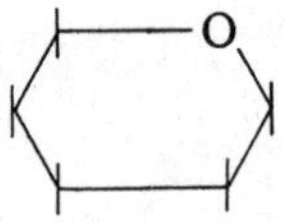

- -

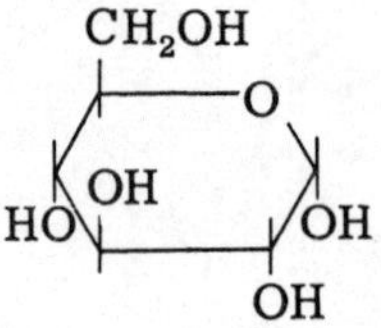

---

20. Write a "shorthand" formula for glucose.

- -

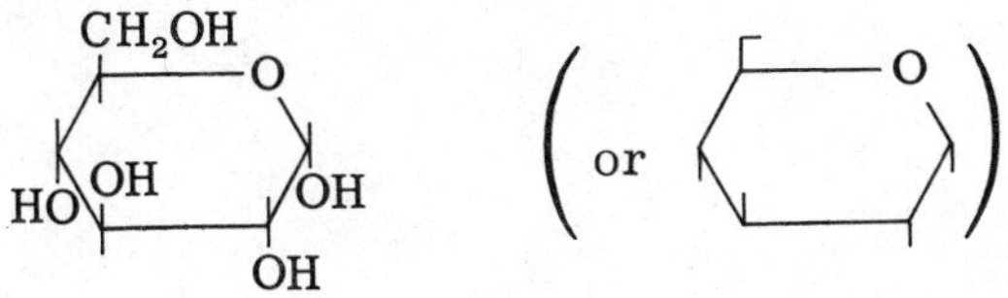

CH_2OH

HO OH OH OH (or)

---

21. What is the difference between galactose and glucose?

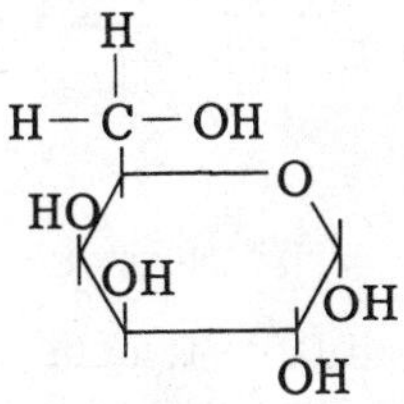

H
H $-$ C $-$ OH
HO OH OH OH

Galactose

H
H $-$ C $-$ OH
HO OH OH OH

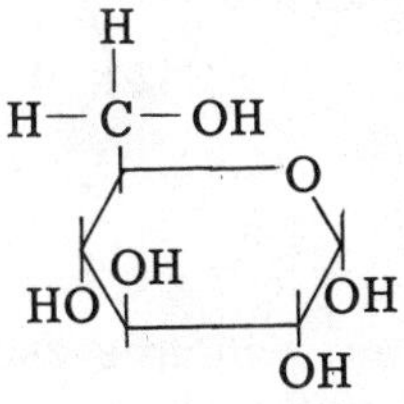

Glucose

- -

Inverted OH on
carbon #4 ———→ HO

H
H $-$ C $-$ OH
OH OH OH

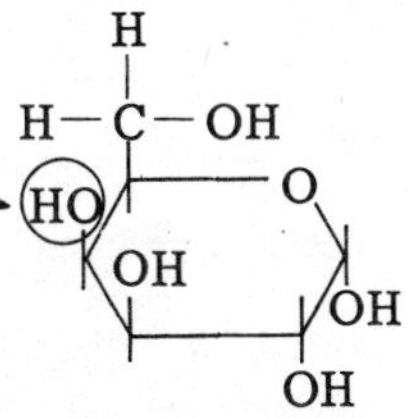

Galactose

H
H $-$ C $-$ OH
HO OH OH OH

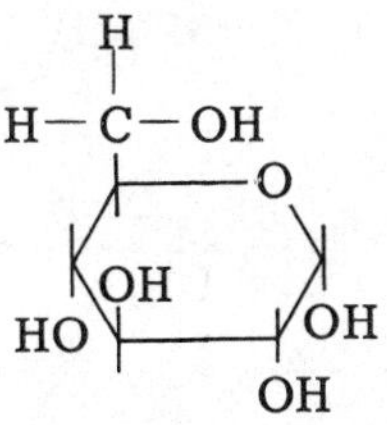

Glucose

(Galactose and glucose can combine to form lactose, the characteristic sugar of milk.)

22. Write the "shorthand" structural formula for fructose.

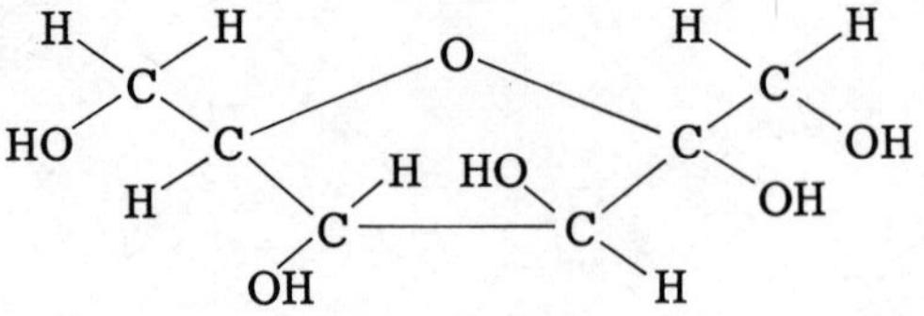

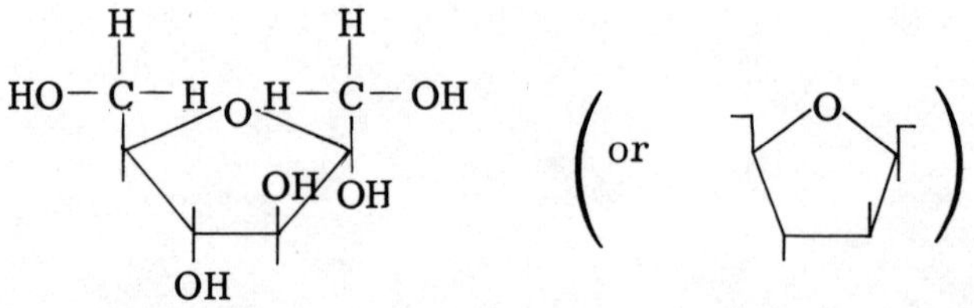

(Fructose is the sugar which is characteristic of fruit; hence, it is commonly called "fruit sugar." It is also an intermediate in respiration and photosynthesis.)

----

23. Which carbon has an "inverted" OH group?

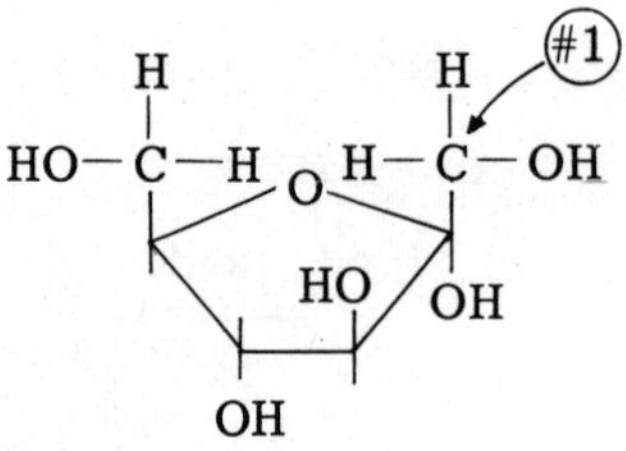

Carbon #3

24. Write the "shorthand" structural formula for fructose.

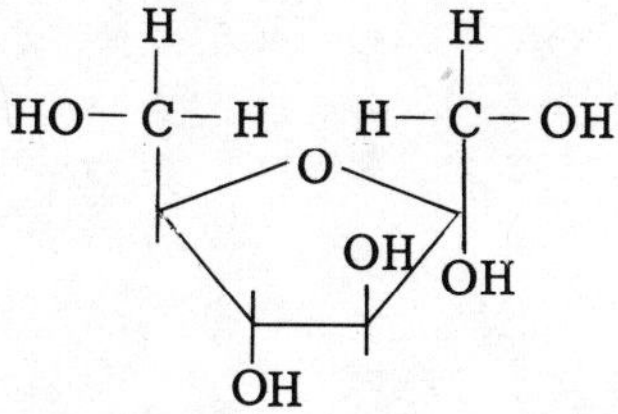

25. Name each of the following:

A.

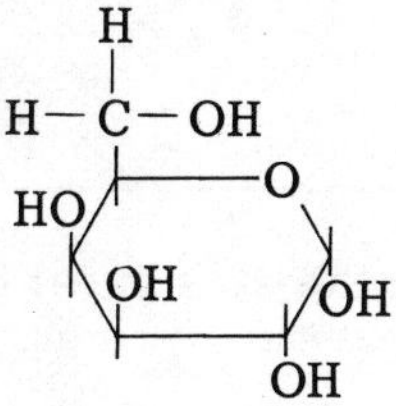

B.

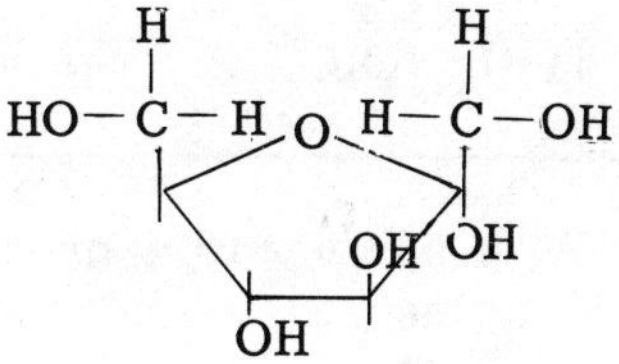

C.

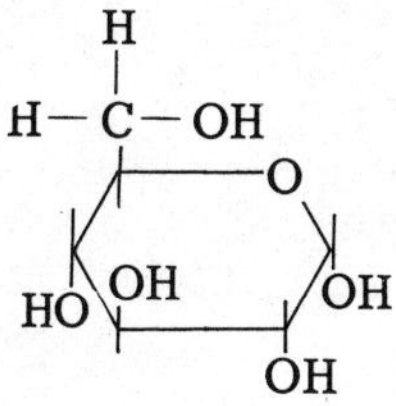

- -

A. galactose
B. fructose
C. glucose

26. Which of the following is lactic acid and which is pyruvic acid?
    (Label)

A.
$$
\begin{array}{c}
H \\
| \\
H-C-OH \\
| \\
C=O \\
| \\
H-C-OH \\
| \\
H-C-OH \\
| \\
H
\end{array}
$$

B.
$$
\begin{array}{c}
H \\
| \\
H-C-H \\
| \\
C=O \\
| \\
C \\
\diagup \diagdown \\
O \quad OH
\end{array}
$$

C.
$$
\begin{array}{c}
O \diagdown \quad \diagup OH \\
C \\
| \\
H-C-OH \\
| \\
H-C-H \\
| \\
H
\end{array}
$$

D.
$$
\begin{array}{c}
H \\
| \\
H-C-OH \\
| \\
H-C-OH \\
| \\
H-C-OH \\
| \\
H
\end{array}
$$

- -

lactic acid — C   pyruvic acid — B

27. Without consulting preceding items, write the structural formula
    for glucose.

- -

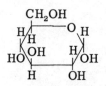

Take at least a 5-minute break before going on to the next unit.

UNIT 7 CARBOHYDRATES II

Monosaccharides or their derivatives may combine to form more complex food storage and structural carbohydrates. The pentose sugars, ribose and deoxyribose, are also used as constituents of the huge molecular chains of nucleic acids, the chemical materials of which genes are made. You will use ribose and deoxyribose to diagram nucleic acid molecules in a later unit. Two molecules of simple sugar may unite to make a disaccharide such as sucrose, or ordinary table sugar. Larger carbohydrates are formed by linking many simple sugars, or related molecules, together. Some of the large carbohydrate molecules you will study are cellulose; chitin, the material of the cuticle of insects and other arthropods; starch, a plant food storage carbohydrate; glycogen, an animal food storage carbohydrate; and mucopolysaccharides, the binding material which helps to cement animal cells together.

Material Covered

Ribose, deoxyribose
Hydrolysis
Disaccharides
   Sucrose
   Maltose
   Cellobiose
   Lactose
   α and β linkages
Polysaccharides
Starch — 1-4 and 1-6 linkages
   Amylose, Amylopectin, Glycogen
Cellulose
Glucosamine
Chitin

1.

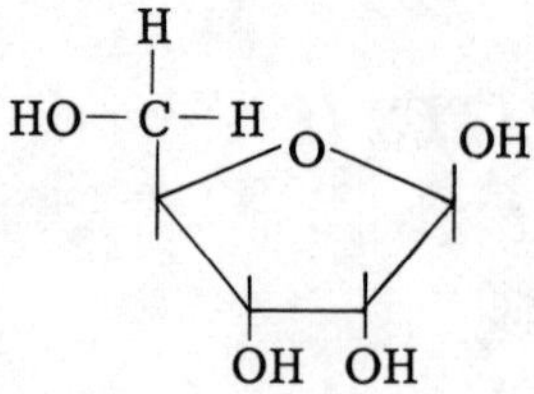

Ribose 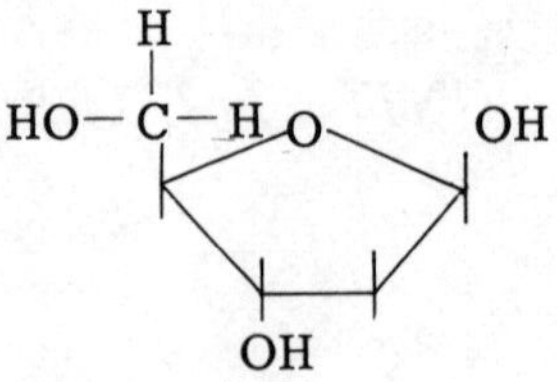   Deoxyribose

How many carbons does each have? What name would apply to ribose and deoxyribose? What is the difference between ribose and deoxyribose? Which carbon has an inverted OH group in ribose?

5
Pentoses
Deoxyribose lacks an $-OH$ group on carbon #2 (i.e., OH is replaced by H).
Carbon #1

---

2. Write the "shorthand" structural formula for ribose and deoxyribose.

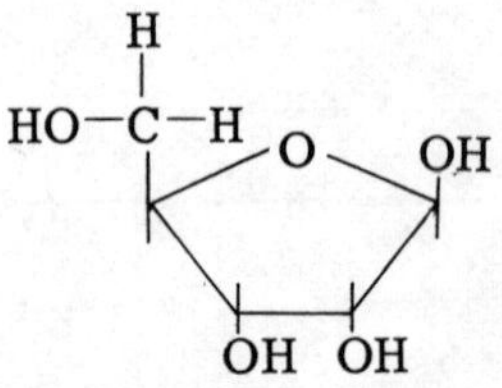

Note: This $-OH$ can be in any position

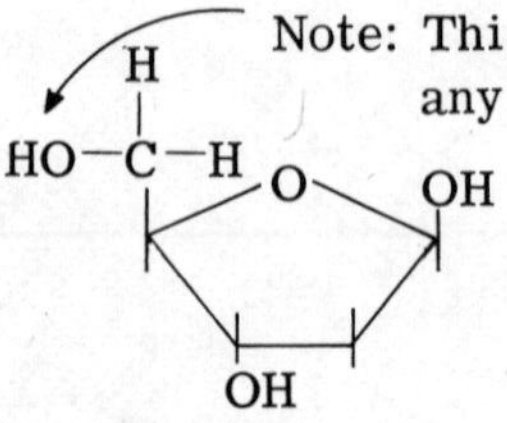

Ribose   Deoxyribose

3. Write an outline structural formula for each of the following:
   Glucose
   Ribose
   Deoxyribose

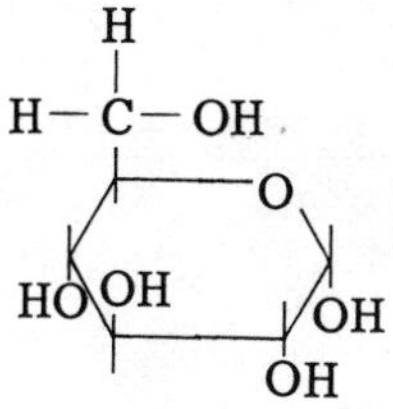

Glucose 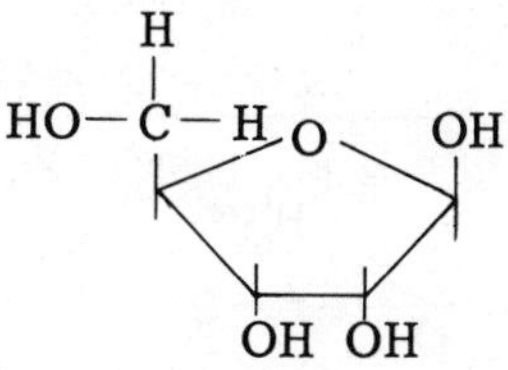   Ribose 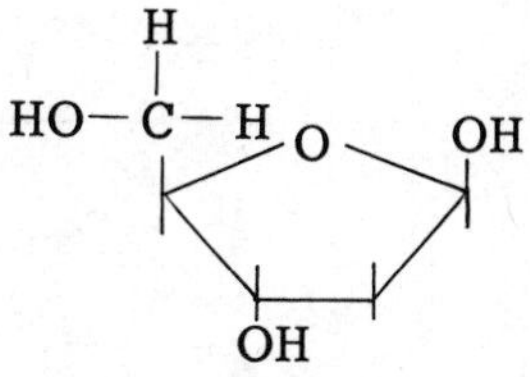   Deoxyribose

_____

4.

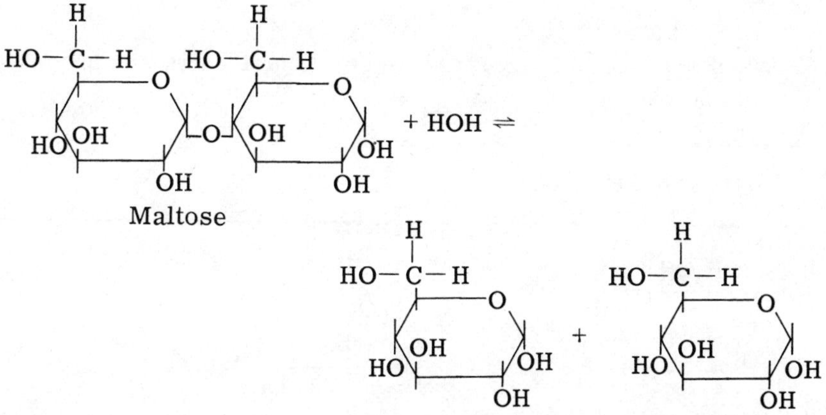

Maltose   + HOH ⇌

This reaction, from left to right, is an example of a *hydrolysis* reaction. What molecule is always added in a hydrolysis reaction? What two molecules are produced by the hydrolysis of maltose?

H_2O (HOH or water)
2 molecules of glucose

5. Similarly:
    2 Glucose ⇌ _____ + _____
    Fill in the blanks.

    Maltose + water (H_2O)

---

6. Glucose is a *mono*saccharide. Maltose is composed of two monosaccharides (2 glucose). What general term would you apply to
   maltose?

----

    *Di*saccharide

7.

    Sucrose

    When sucrose is hydrolyzed, what two molecules are produced?

    Glucose + Fructose

8.

    β glucose   α glucose

    α (Greek alpha)   β (Greek beta). What is the difference between
    α glucose and β glucose?

    β glucose has the H and OH attached to carbon No. 1 inverted. (or
    similar response) (This is also an oversimplification of the phe-
    nomenon of stereoisomerism. Although they appear to be almost
    identical, α and β glucose behave quite differently biochemically.)

9.

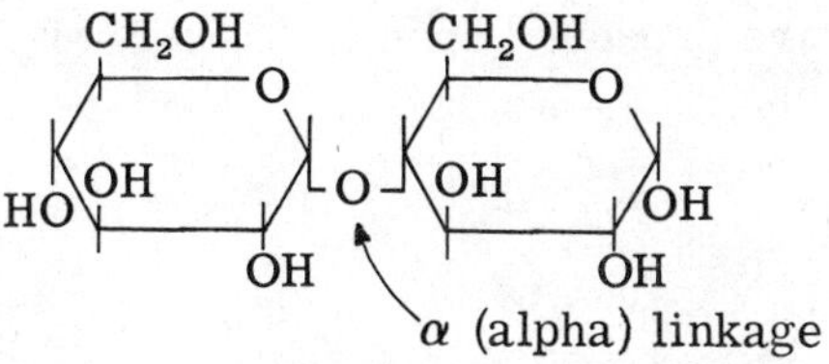

α (alpha) linkage

Maltose

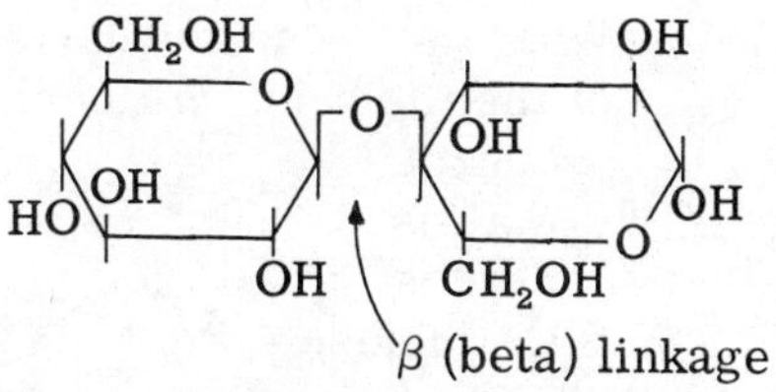

β (beta) linkage

Cellobiose

What two molecules will cellobiose produce upon hydrolysis?
What is the difference between the α and β linkage?

2β glucose
α linkage − 2α glucose; β linkage − 2β glucose. Also, in the β
linkage the second glucose is inverted (upside down). (or similar
response) (Cellobiose is the disaccharide building block of cellulose.)

10.

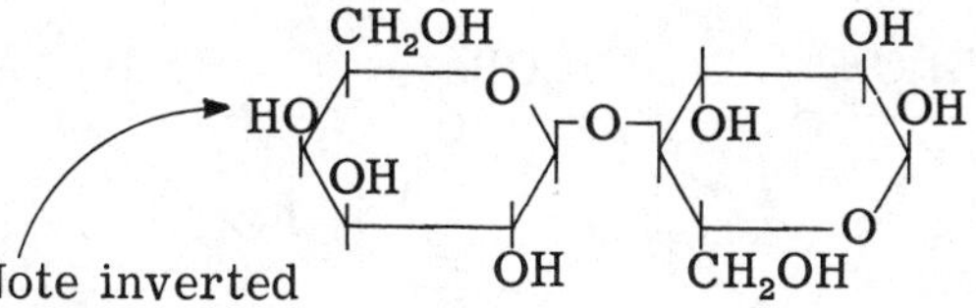

Note inverted
OH on carbon
No. 4

Lactose

What two monosaccharides will be produced by hydrolysis of lactose? What type of linkage is involved?

Glucose + Galactose (actually α glucose and β galactose)
β linkage

11. What two monosaccharides are produced upon hydrolysis of each
of the following disaccharides?
    Sucrose
    Maltose
    Lactose
    Cellobiose
    Which two contain β linkages?

Sucrose — Glucose + Fructose
Maltose — 2 Glucose
Lactose — Glucose + Galactose
Cellobiose — 2 Glucose
β linkages — Lactose and Cellobiose

---

12. Monosaccharide = a simple sugar
Disaccharide = 2 simple sugars
Polysaccharide =

Many simple sugars

13.

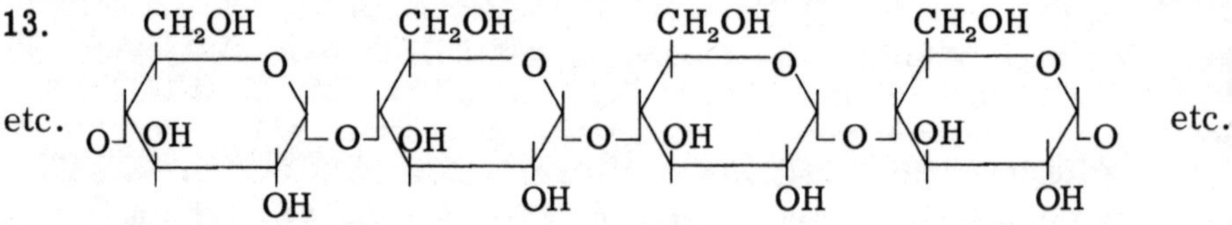

Starch functions in food storage in plants and animals. What general term may be applied to starch? Of what monosaccharide units is starch composed? What type of linkage is involved?

Polysaccharide
Glucose
α

---

14. In the preceding diagram of a starch molecule, which carbons of glucose are linked through O?

The #1 and #4 carbons.

---

15. This is a 1,4α linkage and is characteristic of *amylose* — a straight chain starch. Glucose units can also be linked by a 1,6α linkage. Add another glucose to the molecule below by a 1,6α linkage.

----

or   (or similar response)

16. The linkage you have just written is characteristic of *amylopectin* in plants and *glycogen* in animals. What linkage is characteristic of:

amylose_____

amylopectin and glycogen _____

----

amylose — 1,4 α linkage
amylopectin and glycogen — 1,6 α linkage (in addition to 1,4 α linkages)

---

17. Label the following either amylose or amylopectin and glycogen.

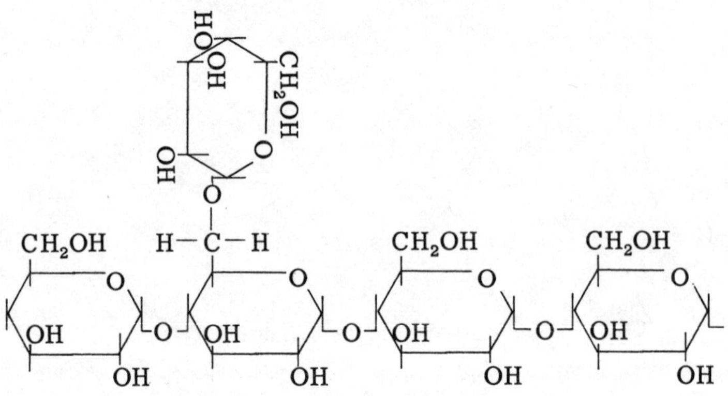

A. (30 or less glucose units)

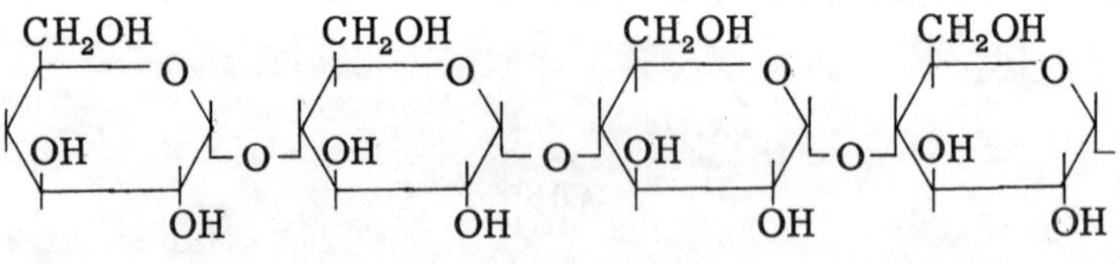

B. (about 1000 glucose units)

A. amylopectin and glycogen
B. amylose

18. Cellulose — constituent of plant cell walls.

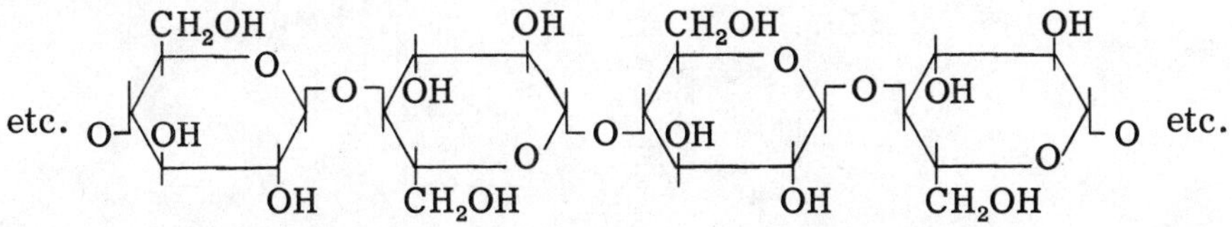

Of what monosaccharide units is cellulose composed? What is the difference between cellulose and starch? Of what disaccharide units is cellulose composed?

β glucose
Cellulose has β linkages (*alternative glucose units are inverted*); starch has α linkages
Cellobiose

----

19. *Glucosamine* is a derivative of glucose in which the OH group of carbon #2 is replaced by an amino group. Write the "shorthand" structural formula for glucosamine.

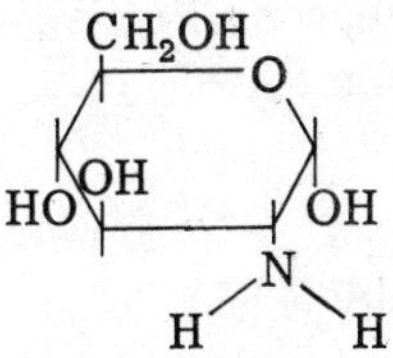

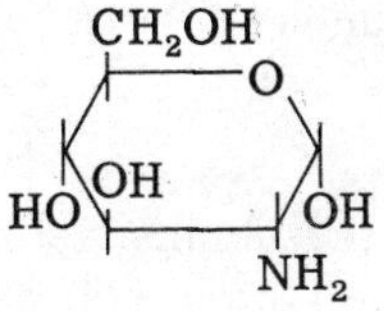

20. Chitin — a constituent of *arthropod cuticle*.

Of what units is chitin composed? What type of linkage is involved?

Glucosamine (actually β glucosamine)
β linkages

---

21. Complete the table:

Polysaccharide	Units	Linkages	Biological Function or Location
Amylose			
Glycogen			
Chitin			
Cellulose			
Amylopectin			

Polysaccharide	Units	Linkages	Biological Function or Location
Amylose	Glucose (ca. 1000)	$1,4\,\alpha$	Plant food storage
Glycogen	Glucose (30 or less)	$1,4\,\alpha$ and $1,6\,\alpha$	Animal food storage
Chitin	Glucosamine	$\beta\,(1,4)$	Arthropod cuticle
Cellulose	Glucose (β)	$\beta\,(1,4)$	Plant cell wall
Amylopectin	Glucose	$1,4\,\alpha$ and $1,6\,\alpha$	Plant food storage

(If you did not fill all the blanks, look up the appropriate information from preceding items and complete the table.)

Take at least a 5-minute break before going on to the next unit.

UNIT *8* AMINO ACIDS

Amino acids are the structural units, or building blocks, of proteins. The importance of proteins as both structural and functional elements in living cells cannot be overemphasized. For example, all enzymes are proteins, and nearly all the reactions in a plant or animal organism are made possible by enzyme action. In order to understand the biochemical potential of protein molecules, it is essential to learn to identify and differentiate the amino acids of which they are composed. You will be asked to learn the seven major classes of amino acids and to assign each amino acid to its appropriate category. This unit will stress the memorization of names and structures to a greater extent than the preceding units.

Material Covered

General formula for an amino acid
Seven classes of amino acids
Structure of cystine
Assignment of each amino acid to the appropriate class.

---

1. An amino acid is a molecule which contains an amino group and an organic acid (carboxyl) group; it may contain other atoms and groups as well. The acid group involves carbon #1. The amino group is attached to carbon #2. The R group varies, and will be dealt with later. Write the general structural formula for an amino acid by completing this skeleton:

   R—C—C
     ↖carbon #1

PANEL B   *The* 19 *Common Amino Acids*
(listed by category)

Hydrocarbon	Hydroxy	Acid

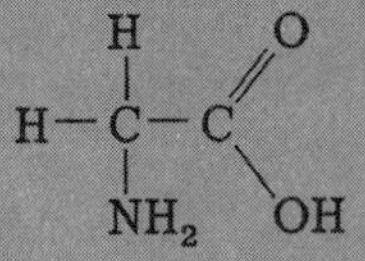

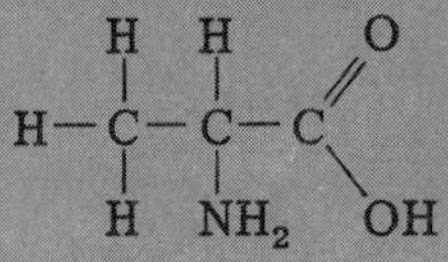

Glycine

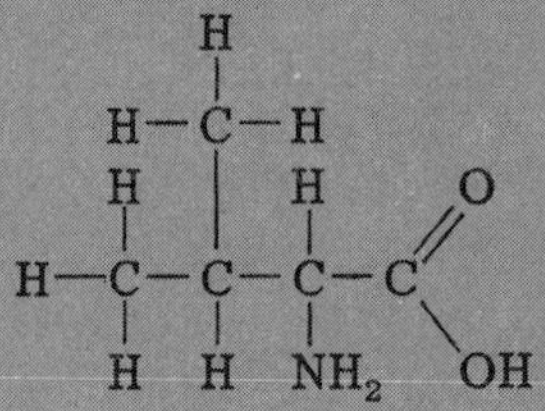

Serine

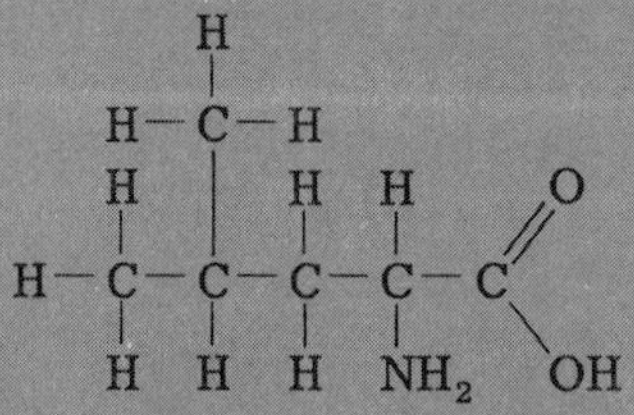

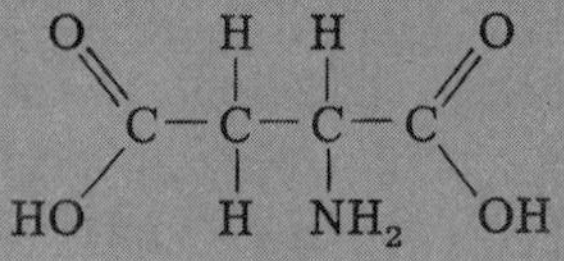

Aspartic Acid

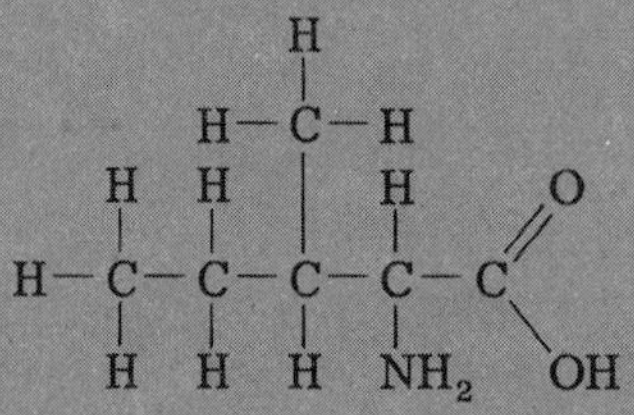

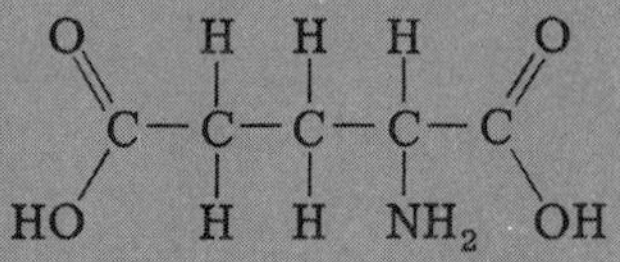

Alanine

Threonine

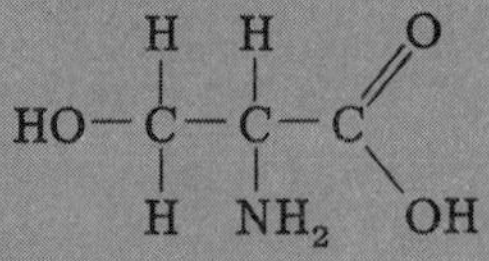

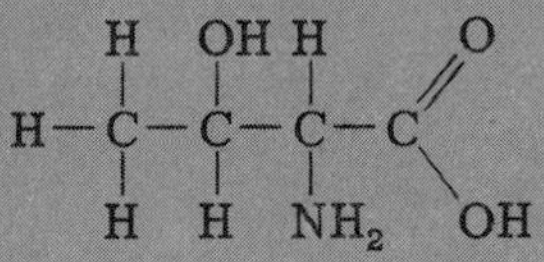

Glutamic Acid

Valine

Sulfur Containing

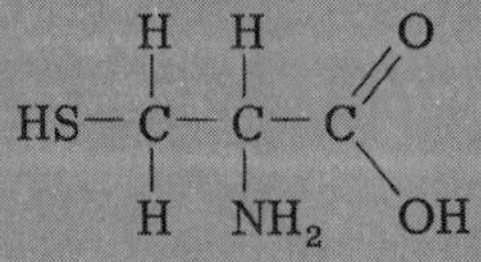

Leucine

Cysteine

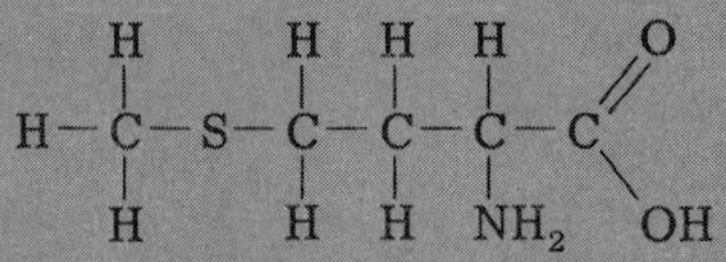

Methionine

Isoleucine

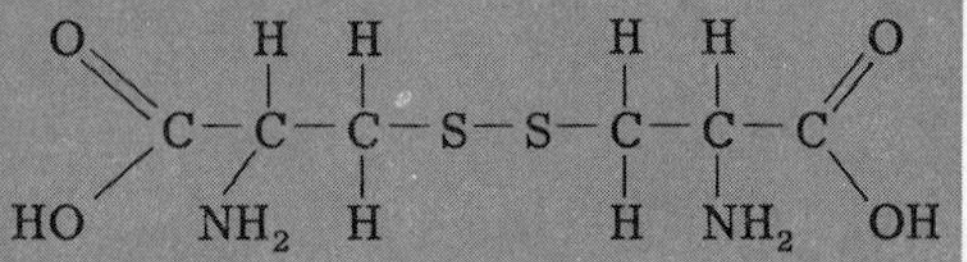

Cystine

Basic

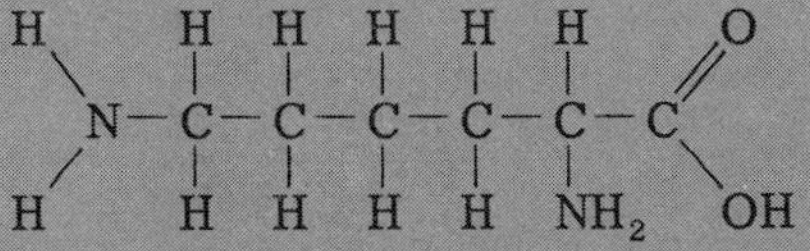

Lysine

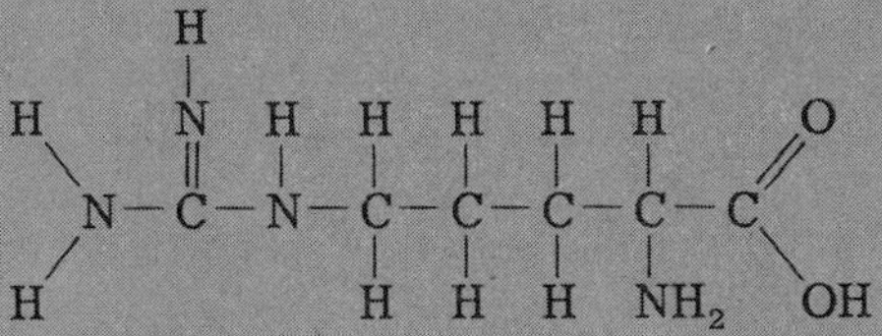

Arginine

Aromatic

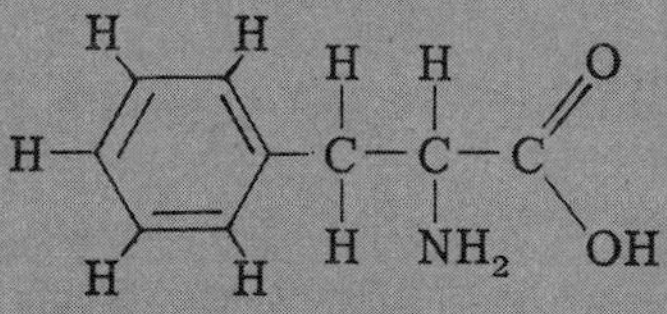

Phenylalanine

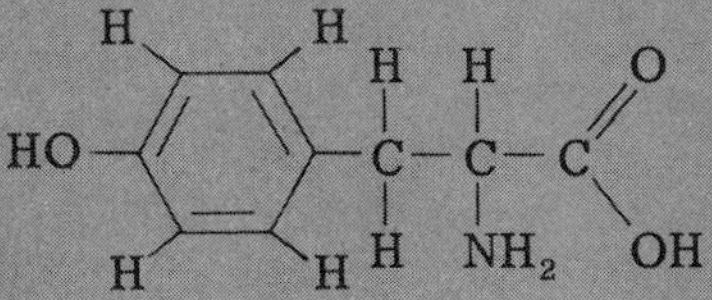

Tyrosine

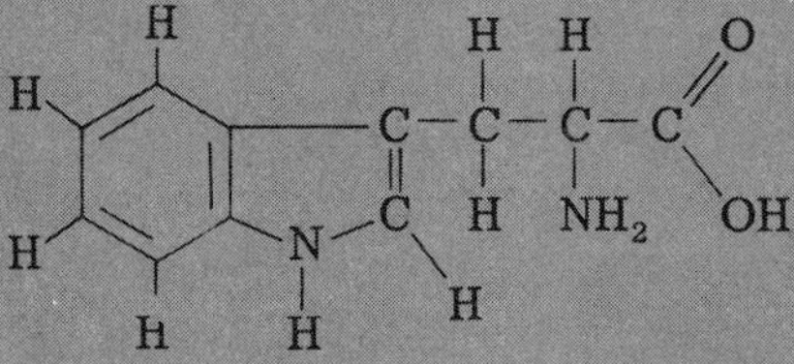

Tryptophan (classified as both
aromatic and heterocyclic)

Heterocyclic

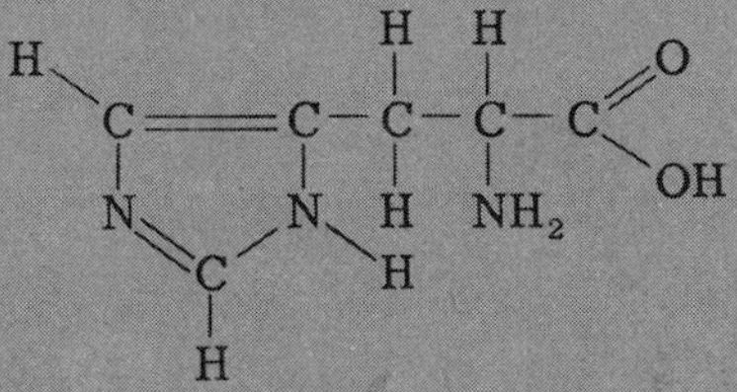

Histidine

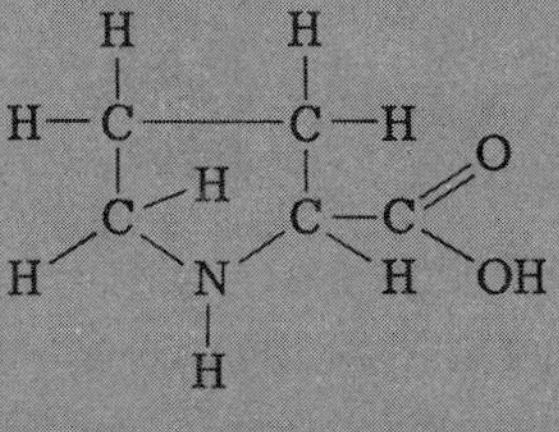

Proline

2. What two chemical groups do all amino acids contain?

Amino (NH_2)
Acid (COOH or CO_2H)

---

3. Write the general formula for an amino acid.

$$R-\overset{\displaystyle H}{\underset{\displaystyle NH_2}{C}}-C\overset{\displaystyle O}{\underset{\displaystyle OH}{}}$$

---

4. Glycine is the amino acid with the simplest structure.

$$H-\overset{\displaystyle H}{\underset{\displaystyle NH_2}{C}}-C\overset{\displaystyle O}{\underset{\displaystyle OH}{}}$$

Pronounced — GLY′ – SEEN
rhymes with sly

What is the R group of Glycine?

− H (or H−)

---

5. Write the structural formula for glycine. (Without consulting Panel B)

$$H-\overset{\displaystyle H}{\underset{\displaystyle NH_2}{C}}-C\overset{\displaystyle O}{\underset{\displaystyle OH}{}}$$

6. Using Panel B when necessary, write the R groups of each of the five hydrocarbon amino acids.

Glycine   Alanine   Valine   Leucine   Isoleucine

Inspect and compare the R groups of these hydrocarbon amino acids. Write the number of carbons in the R group under each.

$$H- \quad -CH_3 \quad CH_3-\overset{\displaystyle CH_3}{\underset{\displaystyle H}{C}}- \quad CH_3-\overset{\displaystyle CH_3}{CH}-CH_2 \quad CH_3-CH_2-\overset{\displaystyle CH_3}{CH}-$$

Glycine	Alanine	Valine	Leucine	Isoleucine
0	1	3	4	4

Pronunciation Drill

AL	— A	— NEEN	Say <u>alanine</u> out loud
as in	as in	rhymes with	three times
Albert	<u>up</u>	<u>seen</u>	

VAY' — LEEN   Say <u>valine</u> out loud
as in   three times
<u>Jay</u>

LOU' — SEEN   Say <u>leucine</u> out loud
                          three times

                          Say <u>isoleucine</u> out loud
                          three times.

<u>Note</u>: The <u>ine</u> of the amino acids is always pronounced <u>een</u>

7. Without consulting preceding items, list the 5 hydrocarbon amino acids.

Glycine, alanine, valine, leucine, isoleucine

---

8. Only two amino acids contain $-OH$ groups, serine and threonine. What are the R groups of each? (Use Panel B)

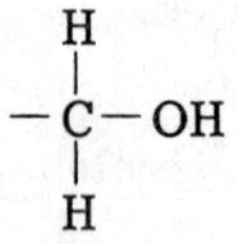

$$\begin{array}{ccc} & H & \\ & | & \\ -&C&-OH \\ & | & \\ & H & \end{array} \qquad \begin{array}{cc} H & H \\ | & | \\ -C&-C-H \\ | & | \\ OH & H \end{array}$$

Serine 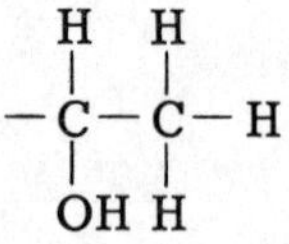   Threonine

Pronounced — SEAR′– EEN
as in
ear

THREE′– O – NEEN

---

9. List the two hydroxy amino acids (do not use Panel B).

Serine and threonine

---

10. Three amino acids contain sulfur — cysteine, cystine, and methionine. Diagram the R groups of cysteine and methionine (use Panel B).

$$
\begin{array}{c}
H \\
| \\
-C-S-H \\
| \\
H
\end{array}
\qquad
\begin{array}{c}
H \quad H \qquad H \\
| \quad\; | \qquad\; | \\
-C-C-S-C-H \\
| \quad\; | \qquad\; | \\
H \quad H \qquad H
\end{array}
$$

Cysteine   Methionine

Pronunciation Drill

CYST' — E — EEN		Say out loud three
as in as in		times
sister bee		
CYST'— EEN		Say out loud three
		times
METH — EYE'— O — NEEN		Say out loud three
as in		times
methyl		

11. Locate the structural formula for cystine on Panel B. Many chemists do not consider cystine as a separate amino acid because it is composed of two cysteines. Copy the structural formula for cystine and circle each of the two cysteine components.

12. What two atoms have been removed from the two cysteine molecules which unite to produce a cystine? (Use Panel B)

Two H atoms

13. Complete the equation (do not use Panel B):

14. List the three amino acids which contain sulfur (do not use Panel B).

Cysteine, cystine, and methionine

---

15. List the amino acids in each of these classes:

Hydrocarbon (5)	Hydroxy (2)	Sulfur containing (3)

Hydrocarbon (5)	Hydroxy (2)	Sulfur containing (3)
Glycine	Serine	Cysteine
Alanine	Threonine	Cystine
Valine		Methionine
Leucine		
Isoleucine		

---

16. Diagram the R groups of the two acid amino acids: aspartic acid and glutamic acid (use Panel B).

Pronounced: ASS — PAR' — TIC
GLUE — TAM' — IC

Aspartic acid   Glutamic acid

---

17. Name the two acid amino acids (do not use Panel B).

Aspartic acid and glutamic acid

---

18. Diagram the R group of the basic (amino) amino acids lysine and argenine.

Pronounced: LIE' — SEEN
ARR' — JEN — EEN

Lysine	Argenine

$$-\overset{\underset{|}{\text{H}}}{\underset{\overset{|}{\text{H}}}{\text{C}}}-\overset{\underset{|}{\text{H}}}{\underset{\overset{|}{\text{H}}}{\text{C}}}-\overset{\underset{|}{\text{H}}}{\underset{\overset{|}{\text{H}}}{\text{C}}}-\overset{\underset{|}{\text{H}}}{\underset{\overset{|}{\text{H}}}{\text{C}}}-\text{NH}_2$$

Lysine

$$-\overset{\underset{|}{\text{H}}}{\underset{\overset{|}{\text{H}}}{\text{C}}}-\overset{\underset{|}{\text{H}}}{\underset{\overset{|}{\text{H}}}{\text{C}}}-\overset{\underset{|}{\text{H}}}{\underset{\overset{|}{\text{H}}}{\text{C}}}-\text{N}-\overset{\text{NH}}{\overset{\|}{\text{C}}}-\text{NH}_2$$

Argenine

---

19. Two other $-NH_2$ containing amino acids are derivatives of aspartic and glutamic acids. Refer to the structural formulae for the R groups of aspartic acid and glutamic acid which you wrote in Item 16. Replace the $-OH$ of the R acid group with $-NH_2$. Label these structures asparagine and glutamine.

Pronounced: ASS — PARE' — A — GEEN
GLUE' — TA — MEEN

$$-\overset{\underset{|}{\text{H}}}{\underset{\overset{|}{\text{H}}}{\text{C}}}-\text{C}\overset{\nearrow\text{O}}{\searrow_{\text{NH}_2}}$$

Asparagine

$$-\overset{\underset{|}{\text{H}}}{\underset{\overset{|}{\text{H}}}{\text{C}}}-\overset{\underset{|}{\text{H}}}{\underset{\overset{|}{\text{H}}}{\text{C}}}-\text{C}\overset{\nearrow\text{O}}{\searrow_{\text{NH}_2}}$$

Glutamine

20. List the four basic amino acids (do not use Panel B).

Lysine, argenine, asparagine, and glutamine

---

21. List the amino acids in each of these classes:

    <u>Acid</u> (2)   <u>Basic</u> (4)

Acid	Basic
Aspartic acid	Lysine
Glutamic acid	Argenine
	Asparagine
	Glutamine

---

22. Diagram the R groups for the two aromatic amino acids phenyl-alanine and tyrosine (use Panel B).

Pronounced: FENIL — ALANINE

        TIRO' — SEEN

        as in <u>tie</u>

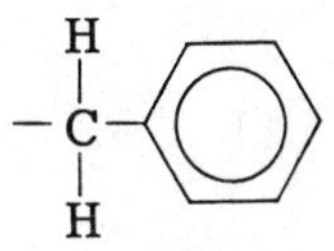

Phenylalanine   Tyrosine

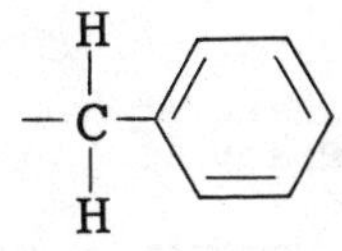

(or similar response)

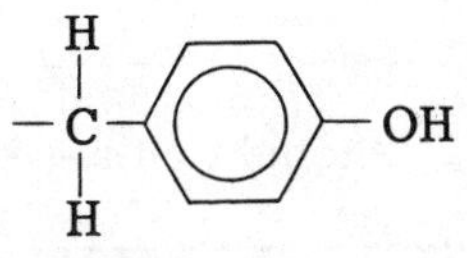

---

23. Diagram the R group for the heterocyclic amino acid tryptophan (use Panel B).

Pronounced: TRIP′ — TOE — FANE
rhymes
with p<u>ai</u>n

- -

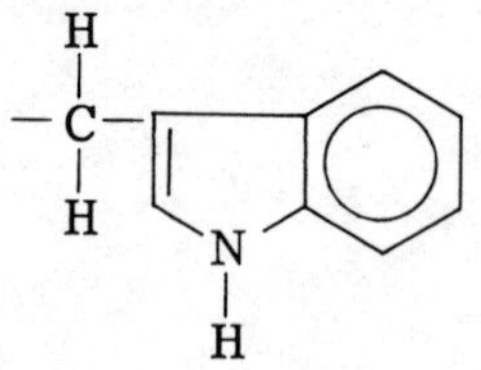

or 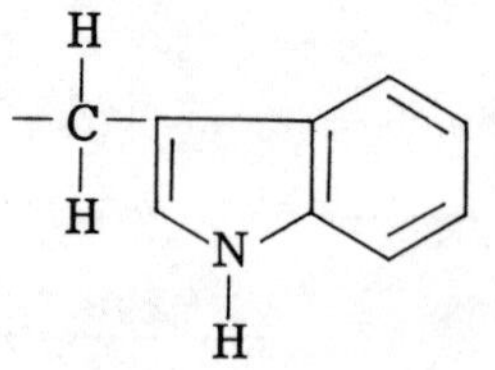   (or similar
                                                         response)

_____

24. Consult your answer to the last question. Does the R group contain an aromatic ring? How many atoms are there in the first (N containing) ring? How many atoms are there in the second ring? How many atoms are common to both rings?

- -

Yes, 5, 6, 2

_____

25. List the three aromatic amino acids.

- -

Phenylalanine, tyrosine, tryptophan

_____

26. Diagram the R group of the heterocyclic amino acid histidine (use Panel B).

Pronounced: HISS′ — TU — DEAN
   as in
   tub

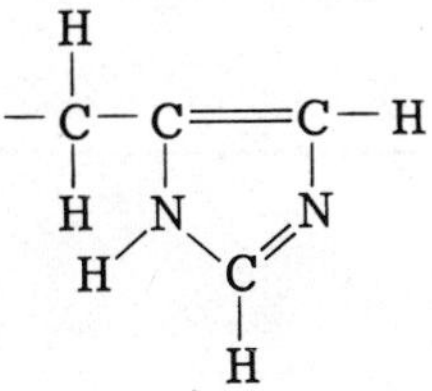

```
      H
      |
   -- C -- C ==== C -- H
      |    |        |
      H    N        N
        H     C
              |
              H
```

----

27. Can you easily write an R group for proline? (Use Panel B.) How many atoms are in the heterocyclic ring? How many C atoms? How many N atoms? How many CH_2 groups?

Pronounced: PRO′ — LEAN

No, 5, 4C, 1N, 3CH_2

----

28. List the three heterocyclic amino acids (do not use Panel B).

Tryptophan, histidine, proline

29. List the amino acids in each class.

   Aromatic (3)   Heterocyclic (3)

Aromatic	Heterocyclic
Phenylalanine	Tryptophan
Tyrosine	Histidine
Tryptophan	Proline

30. List the seven classes of amino acids

Hydrocarbon	Acid	Heterocyclic
Hydroxy	Basic (Amino)	
Sulfur-containing	Aromatic	(any order)

If you omit any, add those left out.

31. Using the classes from your last answer, place the 21 common
amino acids in the correct class. Do this rapidly; do not be concerned if you miss a few.

Alanine	Glutamine	Phenylalanine
Arginine	Glycine	Proline
Asparagine	Histidine	Serine
Aspartic acid	Isoleucine	Threonine
Cysteine	Leucine	Tryptophan
Cystine	Lysine	Tyrosine
Glutamic acid	Methionine	Valine

- -

Hydrocarbon — glycine, alanine, valine, leucine, isoleucine
Hydroxy — serine, threonine
Sulfur containing — cysteine, cystine, methionine
Acid — aspartic acid, glutamic acid
Basic — lysine, arginine, asparagine, glutamine
Aromatic — tyrosine, phenylalanine, tryptophan
Heterocyclic — tryptophan, histidine, proline
If you misplaced any of the amino acids, correct your response.

32. To which class of amino acid does each of the following belong?

Proline_____   Tyrosine_____
Leucine_____   Threonine_____
Lysine _____   Cystine_____
Methionine_____

- -

Proline Heterocyclic   Tyrosine   Aromatic
Leucine Hydrocarbon   Threonine   Hydroxy
Lysine   Basic   Cystine   Sulfur-Containing
Methionine   Sulfur-Containing

Take at least a 5-minute break before going on to the next unit.

UNIT *9* PROTEINS I

Many proteins are important in biological structure — for example, the keratin of hair, collagen of skin and leather, and fibroin of silk. Other proteins function as enzymes, which control or modulate literally all biochemical reactions. The biochemical potential of a protein is determined by its constituent amino acids. You will now learn to link amino acids together to form polypeptides and proteins. The coiling of a protein to form an α helix will also be studied with a paper model.

Material Covered

Peptide unit
Peptide bond
Dipeptide, tripeptide, etc., polypeptides
Protein
Insulin
α-helix
Linus Pauling

---

1. Circle any of the following which are *not* amino acids.

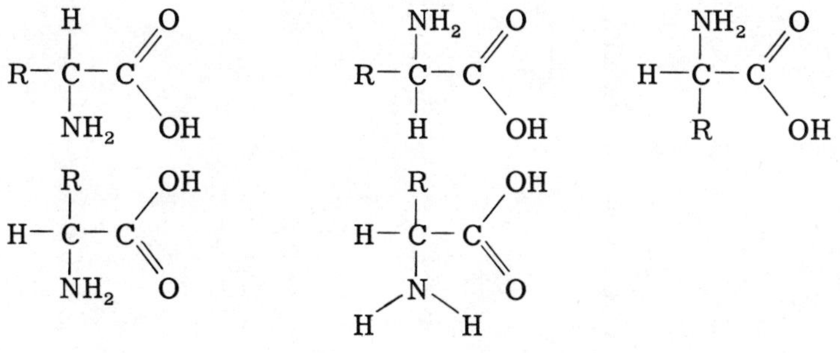

- - - - - - - - - - - - - - - - - - - -

All are amino acids.

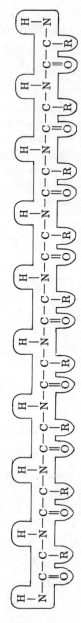

α-helix model. Cut out along line.

2. Circle the H and OH which will be removed as two amino acid molecules are linked. What two *atoms* will then be linked by a covalent bond? What two *groups* are so linked?

$$R-\underset{\underset{H}{\overset{|}{N}}-H}{\overset{\overset{H}{|}}{C}}-C\overset{O}{\underset{OH}{\diagup}} \qquad \underset{H}{\overset{H}{\diagdown}}N-\underset{\underset{H}{\overset{|}{}}}{\overset{\overset{R}{|}}{C}}-C\overset{O}{\underset{OH}{\diagup}}$$

$$R-\underset{NH_2}{\overset{\overset{H}{|}}{C}}-C\overset{O}{\underset{\boxed{OH}}{\diagup}} \qquad \underset{\boxed{H}}{\overset{H}{\diagdown}}N-\underset{\underset{H}{\overset{|}{}}}{\overset{\overset{R}{|}}{C}}-C\overset{O}{\underset{OH}{\diagup}}$$

C and N
Carboxyl (acid) and amino

----

3. Complete the reaction (you may consult the preceding item if necessary):

$$R-\underset{NH_2}{\overset{\overset{H}{|}}{C}}-C\overset{O}{\underset{OH}{\diagup}} \quad + \quad R-\underset{NH_2}{\overset{\overset{H}{|}}{C}}-C\overset{O}{\underset{OH}{\diagup}} \quad \rightleftharpoons \qquad\qquad +$$

$$R-\underset{NH_2}{\overset{\overset{H}{|}}{C}}-\overset{\overset{O}{\|}}{C}-\underset{H}{\overset{}{N}}-\underset{H}{\overset{\overset{R}{|}}{C}}-C\overset{O}{\underset{OH}{\diagup}} \quad + H_2O$$

4. Each amino acid in this structure is a *peptide*. Circle each peptide unit in the *dipeptide* molecule below. What two atoms are joined in the peptide bond?

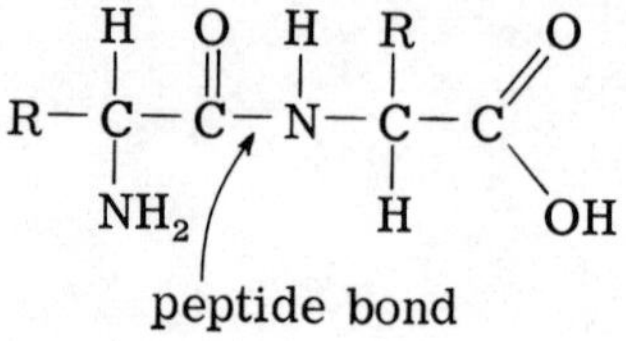

peptide bond

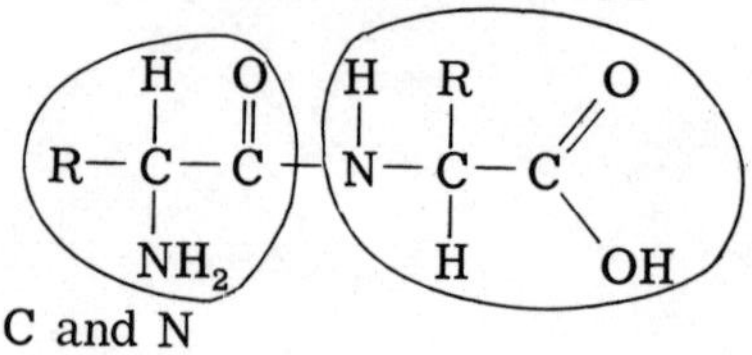

C and N

---

5. How many amino acid molecules would be involved in the formation of the following:

Dipeptide_____

Tripeptide_____

Pentapeptide_____

Octapeptide_____

Polypeptide_____

Dipeptide_____2_____

Tripeptide_____3_____

Pentapeptide_____5_____

Octapeptide_____8_____

Polypeptide___many___

6. Write the equation for the formation of a peptide bond between two amino acids of general structural formulae. Label the peptide bond.

- -

$$H-\underset{\underset{NH_2}{|}}{\overset{\overset{R}{|}}{C}}-\overset{\overset{O}{\parallel}}{C}\diagdown_{OH} \;+\; \underset{\underset{H}{}}{\overset{\overset{H}{\diagdown}}{N}}-\underset{\underset{H}{|}}{\overset{\overset{R}{|}}{C}}-\overset{\overset{O}{\parallel}}{C}\diagdown_{OH} \;\rightleftharpoons\; H-\underset{\underset{NH_2}{|}}{\overset{\overset{R}{|}}{C}}-\overset{\overset{O}{\parallel}}{C}-\underset{\underset{H}{|}}{\overset{\overset{H}{|}}{N}}-\underset{\underset{H}{|}}{\overset{\overset{R}{|}}{C}}-\overset{\overset{O}{\parallel}}{C}\diagdown_{OH} \;+\; H_2O$$

peptide bond

7. Write the general structural formula for a pentapeptide. Circle each peptide unit.

- -

$=O$ or H or R

can be oriented up or down.

8. What is the repeating sequence of atoms in the backbone of a polypeptide? (Consult your last answer.)

- -

$$-N-C-C-\!\!\!-N-C-C-\!\!\!-N-C-C-\; \text{etc.}$$

9. For convenience, we might diagram a polypeptide thus:

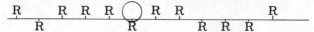

Each R = the R group of one amino acid. How many peptides are involved in this structure? What atoms would the area included within the circle represent? (Use a structural formula.)

- -

12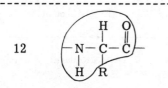

_____

10.

```
                          O    OH
                           \\  /
                            C                        OH
                                                     |
         H          H— C —H              H— C —H
         |           |                              |
  H— C —H      H— C —H        H— C —H        H— C —H
   |            |              |
  S— H          H             H— C —H
                               |                    ⬡
 Cysteine                     H— C —H
 (example)                     |
                              H— C —H
                               |
                              NH₂
      A.       B.       C.            D.            E.        F.
```

In this heptapeptide, label each peptide unit with its appropriate amino acid name (you may consult Panel B).

- -

A. Glycine   D. Lysine
B. Alanine   E. Serine
C. Aspartic acid   F. Phenylalanine

11. A *protein* molecule is a large polypeptide. The size varies from about 50 peptide units to thousands, with several hundred peptides the most common number. Which of the following *could* be proteins? (Assume 1 peptide = m.w. of 100.)

Molecular Weight

96
256
1,420
8,460
22,400
465,000
4,200,000

96	No		8460	Yes (84± peptide units)
256	No		22,400	Yes (224± peptide units)
1420	No	(14± peptide units)	465,000	Yes (4650± peptide units)
			4,200,000	Yes

12. What is the approximate molecular weight range of proteins? What are the "building blocks" of proteins?

5,000 to over a million (or approximate equivalent) amino acids (peptides).

13. This is a part of the protein insulin (the pancreatic hormone which prevents diabetes):

$$\underset{\substack{|\\ NH_2}}{Phe} - Val - \underset{\substack{|\\ NH_2}}{Asp} - \underset{\substack{|\\ NH_2}}{Glu} - His - Leu - \underset{\substack{|\\ SH}}{Cy} - Gly - Ser - His - Leu - Val \rceil$$

$$\lfloor Glu - Ala \quad etc.$$

List the amino acids (peptides) in order from left to right. (Guess if you are not sure.)

- -

Phenylalanine	Leucine	Histidine
Valine	Cysteine (not cystine	Leucine
Asparagine	which is	Valine
Glutamine	Cys−S−S−Cys)	Glutamic acid
Histidine	Glycine	Alanine
	Serine	etc.

14. Another diagram of insulin is as follows:

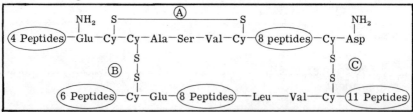

Circle each cystine. How many amino acids does each backbone chain contain? (Count each cysteine as one unit.) How many amino acids does the insulin molecule contain? (Count each cysteine as one unit.)

- -

Each Cy−S−S−Cy (total of 3)
Top − 21
Bottom − 30
Total − 51

15. In the diagram of the insulin molecule, which disulfide bonds (A, B, or C) are intrachain bonds? (Hint: What is the difference between *intra*murals and *inter*collegiate athletics?) Which disulfide bonds are interchain bonds?
Is insulin composed of one or two polypeptides?

Intrachain — A
Interchain — B and C
two

---

16. Think back to the definitions of bonding. Can a bond really be as long as S—S bond "A"?
In the insulin diagram, if the two cysteines are joined by disulfide bond "A", is the chain between them folded or straight? How many terminal —NH_2 groups does insulin have? How many terminal —COOH groups does insulin have?

No   folded   two   two

---

17. Cut out the α-helix model (α = alpha). Note that this model does not contain all the atoms in a polypeptide chain. Diagram a short segment of a polypeptide chain and circle the atoms which are omitted in the model.

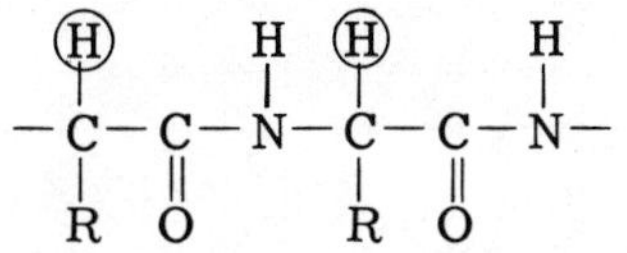

18. Fold out (up) the R groups on the α-helix model. Which of the remaining atoms in the polypeptide chain can participate in H bonding?

The H in $-N-H$
The O in $C=O$

---

19. *From the right*, locate the *first* O and the *fifth* H. Bend the left
end of the model down and to the right to form a spiral (helix)
— matching the fifth H to the first O, thus

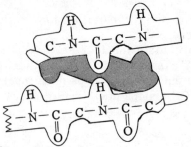

What type of bond can form here?

H bond

---

20. Grasp this H bond (the $=O$ *and* H) between the thumb and fore-
finger of your right hand. Continue to spiral the model, matching
each $\overset{\|}{O}$ with each H to form H bonds. How many H bonds (includ-
ing the one under your left thumb) does this polypeptide chain
form?

6

21. This structure for a protein, the α helix, was first postulated by
Dr. *Linus Pauling* in 1951. He received the Nobel Prize in Chemistry in 1954 for this brilliant achievement. (*Remember Pauling's
name.*) Note that the R groups (bent out) literally "bristle out"
from all sides of the α helix. What would you predict as to the
ability of an α-helical protein to react with adjacent molecules.

Great reactivity due to R groups.

---

22. What term is applied to the polypeptide configuration you have
just been dealing with? This structure is characteristic of some
proteins but not all proteins. Who first set forth the idea of this
structure?

α helix
Dr. Linus Pauling

Take at least a 5-minute break before going on to the next unit.

UNIT *10* PROTEINS II

The structure of a protein molecule is extremely important in determining its biological activity. Biochemists recognize four levels or types of structure within a protein. These levels of structure are designated very simply: primary, secondary, tertiary, and quaternary. You have already dealt with the first two levels of structure as you formed peptide bonds and constructed the α helix. Next, we shall explore additional levels of the structural organization of proteins and will place special emphasis on the types of bonding involved in each. We shall also discuss the combination of non-protein molecules or groups with a protein to form a biologically active molecule, as occurs with many enzymes. Basic proteins will receive some attention because of their significance in chromosome structure.

Material Covered

Primary structure
Secondary structure
Tertiary structure
Quaternary structure (types of bonding involved in each)
Conjugated proteins
Prosthetic groups
Denaturation (agents)
Basic proteins

1. The insulin diagram illustrates what is called the *primary structure* of proteins (see Unit 9, Item 14). The α helix illustrates what is called the *secondary structure* of proteins. Which (primary or secondary) structure is defined by listing a specific sequence of amino acids? Which includes structure imposed by the S—S bonds of cystine? Which involves the coiling of a single polypeptide chain, stabilized by H bonds?

Primary structure; primary structure; secondary structure. *Note*: Additional types of secondary structure, such as the pleated sheet and other helical patterns, do occur, but this text will restrict consideration to the α helix.

2. What two factors are involved in the primary structure of proteins?

Amino acid sequence and S—S bonds of cystine.

3. What type of structure (primary or secondary) is involved in the α helix? What type of bonding is involved in the α helix? Are the peptide units which are bonded together in the α helix close together (less than 5 amino acid units apart) or far apart?

Secondary, H bonding, close together (actually between 3 and 4 units apart).

4. How would you define secondary structure?

- -

Secondary structure involves the coiling of a polypeptide chain
into an α helix which is stabilized by H bonding. (or similar
response)

5. In most proteins only part of the polypeptide chain is coiled in the
α-helix configuration.

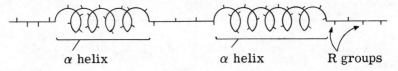

α helix   α helix   R groups

Label the two portions of the chain which exhibit secondary
structure.

- -

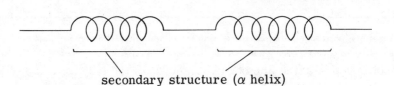

secondary structure (α helix)

6. The preceding polypeptide chain can be folded and twisted further. (Compare with the preceding item)

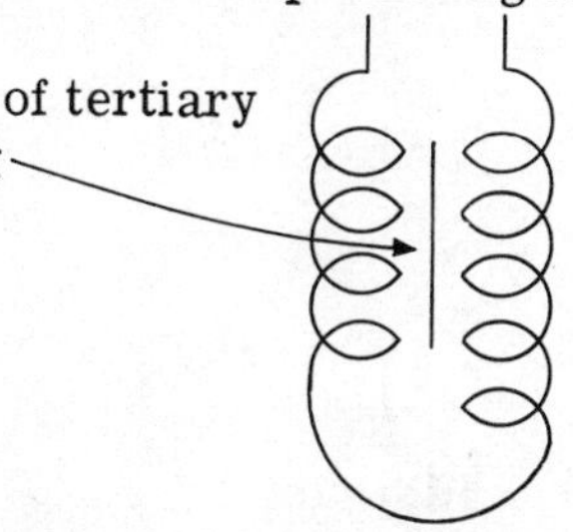

Region of tertiary
bonding

I ← approximate length of one peptide unit.

The R groups have been omitted from the diagram for simplicity.

This is an example of *tertiary* structure. In tertiary bonding, are the amino acids involved close together (less than 5 amino acid units apart) or far apart (more than 5 amino acid units apart in the primary structure)?

- -

Far apart.

---

7. There is little direct evidence concerning the nature of tertiary bonding. However, the following types of bonds are thought to be involved:

Disulfide bonds. These are a part of the primary structure, they also are involved in stabilizing the folding of tertiary structure.

H bonds. Between R groups.

Hydrophobic bonds. Between R groups of the hydrocarbon amino acid units. (see Panel B)

Ionic bonds (salt linkages). Between ⊕ and ⊖ charged R groups or end groups of the polypeptide chain.

What part of the amino acid units are usually involved in tertiary bonding?

- -

R groups

---

8. Between what two peptide units could a *disulfide bond* be formed?

- -

Two cysteine units (to form cystine)

---

9. The following groups play the most significant role in the *H bonding* of tertiary structure:

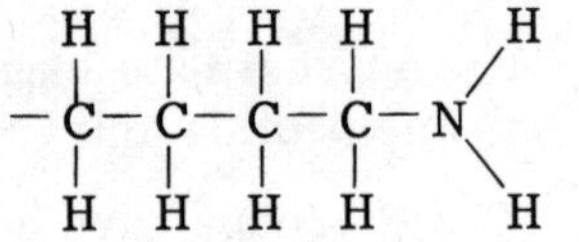

Lysine

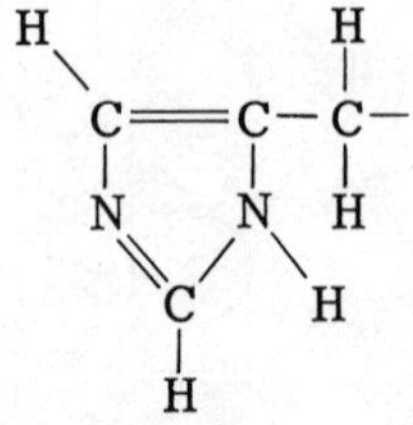

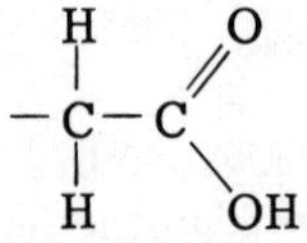

Aspartic Acid

Histidine

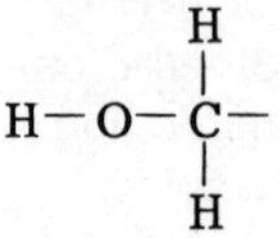

Serine

Diagram the H bond for each pair of R groups. (lysine — histidine) (aspartic acid — serine).

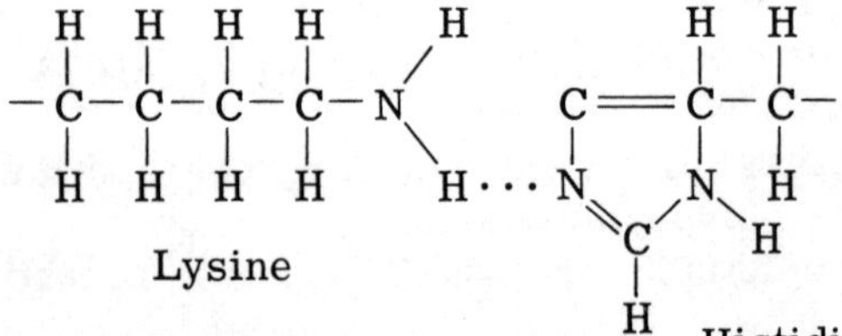

Lysine

Histidine (either H of the NH_2 group may be used)

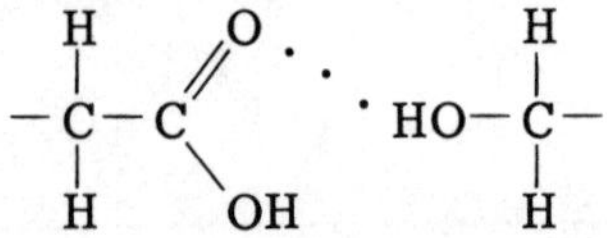

Aspartic acid   Serine

10. List the amino acids whose R groups could participate in *hydrophobic bonding* in the tertiary structure of a protein (consult Panel B).

Alanine, valine, leucine, isoleucine, phenylalanine, tryptophan, and proline.
(Do not be concerned if you did not include all in the list. Check Panel C for those which you did not include to see if you concur with their inclusion.)

---

11. There are seven amino acid groups which can bear a charge (become ions) at physiological pH (acid concentration) (do not worry about the mechanism of ion formation at this time).

Group	Charge
Terminal $-NH_2$	+
Aspartic acid ($-COOH$)	−
Lycine ($-NH_2$)	+
Glutamic acid ($-COOH$)	−
Arginine ($-NH_2$)	+
Histidine ($=N$)	+
Terminal $-COOH$	−

Which of these *could* form an ionic bond with aspartic acid?

----

terminal $-NH_2$
lysine ($-NH_2$)
arginine ($-NH_2$)
histidine ($=N$)

---

12. What four types of bonding are thought to play a part in tertiary structure?

S—S bonds, H bonds, hydrophobic bonds, ionic bonds.

---

13. Define the tertiary structure of a protein.

Tertiary structure refers to the folding of a protein molecule which is stabilized by bonds between distant (5 or more polypeptide chain units apart) peptides. Bonds involved are probably hydrogen, hydrophobic, S—S, and ionic. (or similar response)

---

14. Which components (amino, carboxyl, or R groups) are responsible for the tremendous reactivity of a protein molecule?

R groups

---

15. Some large proteins are made up of folded protein (polypeptide) subunits. The aggregation of the subunits in these cases is termed quaternary structure. Quaternary structure is maintained by the same four types of bonding which were involved in tertiary structure. What types of bonds are thus involved in quaternary structure? For example,

etc.
subunits

S—S bonds, H bonds, hydrophobic bonds, ionic bonds (salt bridges).

---

16. Define quaternary structure.

Quaternary structure involves the bonding between subunits in some large proteins. (or similar answer)

---

17. List and define briefly the four levels of protein structure.

Primary structure — amino acid sequence; includes S—S bonds.
Secondary structure — hydrogen bonding between nearby amino
  acid units to produce a coiling or twisting or the polypeptide
  chain (e.g., α helix).
Tertiary structure — bonding between (reasonably) distant amino
  acid units to cause the folding of a protein molecule; involves
  S—S, H, hydrophobic, and ionic bonds.
Quaternary structure — bonding between subunits of a large protein; same types of bonds as tertiary structure.

18. Hemoglobin, the pigment of mammalian red blood cells, is composed of: globin (a polypeptide) + heme (a non-protein iron-con-
taining group). Hemoglobin is a *conjugated protein*. What would
you suspect to be the difference between *simple* and *conjugated*
proteins?

Simple proteins are polypeptides.
Conjugated proteins contain peptide units + a non-protein group.

19. The non-protein group of a conjugated protein is called a *prosthetic group*. Which component of hemoglobin is the prosthetic group?

Heme

_____

20. What term is applied to each?
    A. a protein made up of a polypeptide chain only.
    B. a protein made up of a polypeptide + a non-polypeptide group.
    C. The non-polypeptide group of "B".

A. simple protein   B. conjugated protein   C. prosthetic group

_____

21. Many biologically active proteins are folded into a precise tertiary structure essential to their biological activity. A change in tertiary structure usually causes the protein to become biologically inactive. A structurally inactivated protein is said to be *denatured*. In your own words what causes the denaturation of a protein?

A change in the tertiary structure of the protein. (or similar response)

_____

22. Heat, organic solvents, acids, bases, and other "harsh" treatments will cause protein denaturation. These agents also facilitate the disruption of H bonds. What is the probable cause of denaturation by these agents?

Disruption of the H bonds of *tertiary structure*. (or similar response)

_____

23. What term applies to a change in the tertiary structure of a protein which produces a loss of biological activity? List as many
agents or treatments as you can which will cause this change.

- -

Denaturation
Agents: heat, organic solvents, acids, bases (or other "harsh"
treatments)

---

24. In your own words, define the denaturation of a protein.

- -

Protein denaturation involves a change in the tertiary structure
which causes a loss of biological activity. (Due to disruption of
H bonds; agents — heat, organic solvents, acids, bases, etc.) (or
similar response)

---

25. What amino acid units should be characteristic of a *basic protein* (polypeptide chain)? (You may consult Panel B.)

- -

Lysine and arginine (and asparagine and glutamine) (the basic
amino acids). (or similar response)

---

26. Below the percentages of amino acid units of two proteins are listed:

Amino Acid Unit	Gelatin	Histone
Alanine	9.3	6.9
Arginine	8.6	17.4
Aspartic acid	6.7	5.7
Glutamic acid	11.2	4.3
Glycine	26.9	5.1
Histidine	0.7	2.7
Isoleucine	1.8	20.8
Leucine	3.4	5.2
Lysine	4.6	10.2
Phenylalanine	2.6	4.1
Proline	14.8	4.0
Serine	3.2	4.7
Threonine	2.2	4.8
Tyrosine	1.0	3.3
Valine	3.3	3.2

(Adapted from Canterow and Schepartz, *Biochemistry*, Saunders 1962)

Which of the two is a basic protein?

Histone (note the relative levels of lysine and arginine).

27. Define a basic protein.

A basic protein contains a high percentage of lysine and arginine units. (or similar response)

28. Does the table of item 26 specify the primary structure of either protein?

No (the *specific order* of amino acids is not specified).

29. Generally speaking are proteins biochemically reactive? What components of the polypeptide chain are responsible for this reactivity?

Yes. Reactivity is due to the R groups of the amino acid units.

Take at least a 5-minute break before going on to the next unit.

REVIEW UNITS 6-10

This review unit, like the last one, should provide a check on your level of retention. Again, be careful to go back to the original items to review any material that is not clear or which gives you difficulty.

1. What word ending is characteristic of a
   _____ salt
   _____ sugar
   _____ acid
   How many carbon atoms does each of the following contain?
   _____ triose
   _____ nonose
   _____ pentose

   -

-ate	salt	3	triose
-ose	sugar	9	nonose
-ic	acid	5	pentose

   Review: Unit 3, Items 16-17
   Unit 6, Items 3-6

2. Write the general (empirical) formula for a carbohydrate.

   -

   $C_n(H_2O)_n$ *Review: Unit 6, Items 1-2*

3. Write the structural formula for glucose.

- -

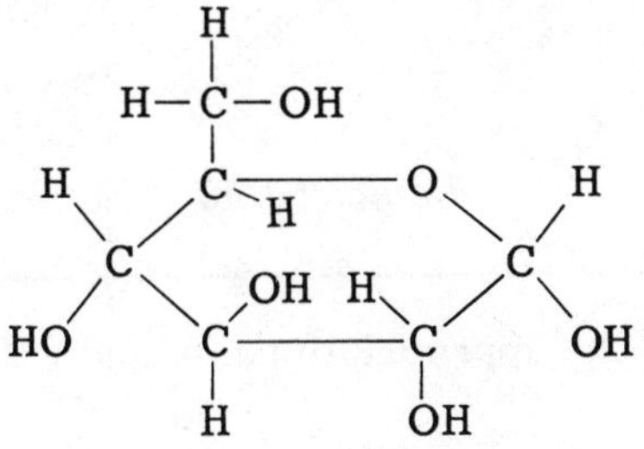

$$
\begin{array}{c}
\text{H} \\
| \\
\text{H}-\text{C}-\text{OH} \\
\end{array}
$$

Review: Unit 6, Items 14-16

4. Label each of the following:

A.

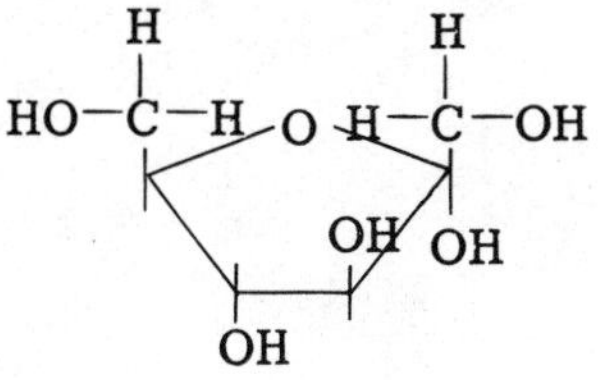

C.

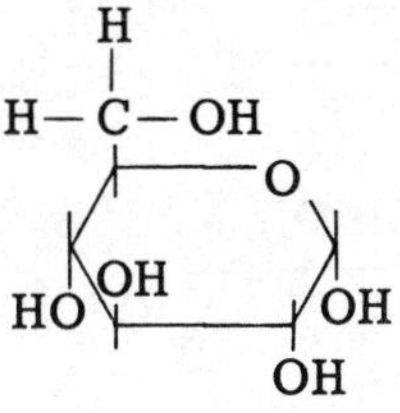

B.

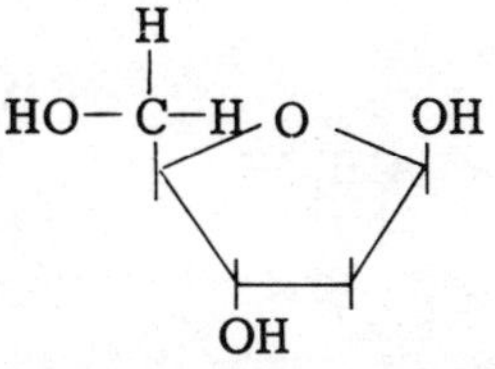

D.

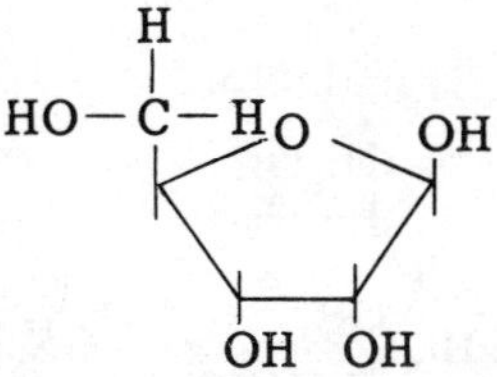

- -

A. Fructose   C. Glucose
B. Deoxyribose   D. Ribose

Review: Unit 7, Items 1-5

5. Diagram the shorthand structural formula for ribose.

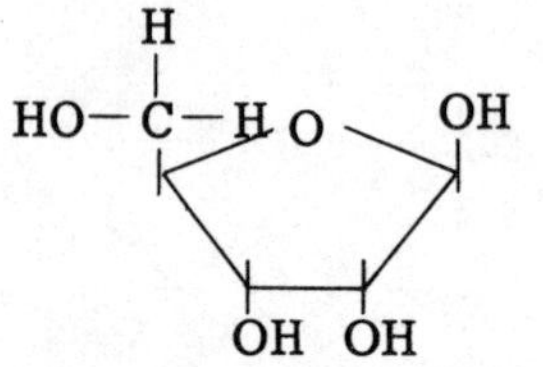

Review: Unit 7, Items 1-2

6. Label each of the following with the appropriate name and with the appropriate linkage (α or β).

A.

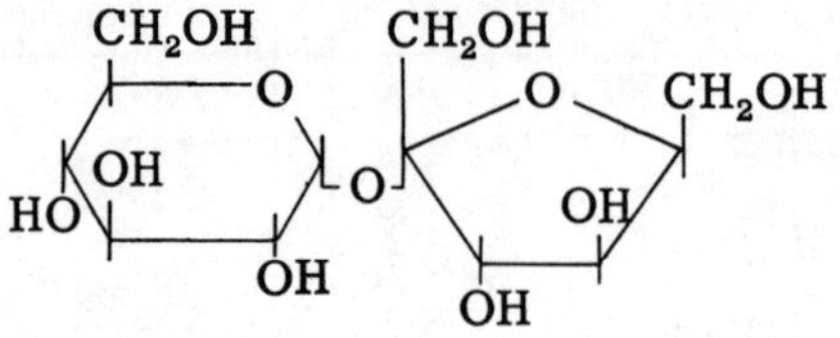

B.

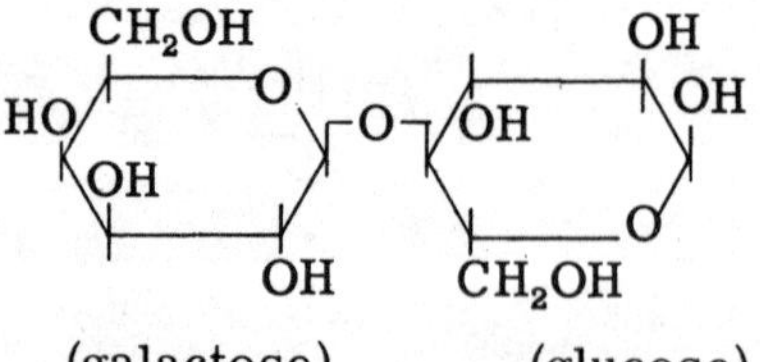

(galactose)   (glucose)

C.

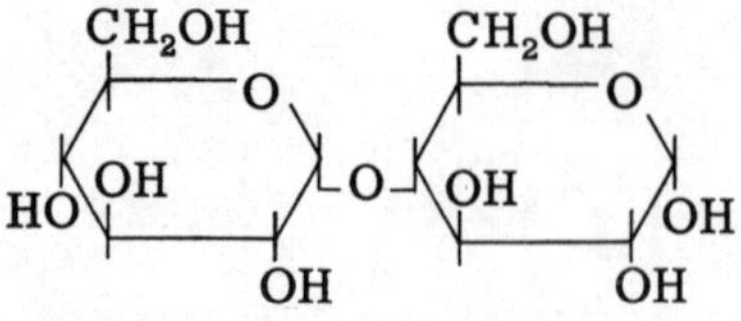

D.

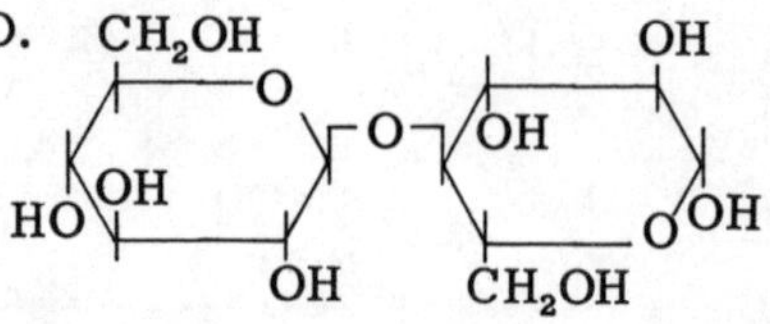

A. Sucrose (α)   C. Maltose (α)
B. Lactose (β)   D. Cellobiose (β)

Review: Unit 7, Items 6-12

7. Complete the table:

Polysaccharide	Monosaccharide Units	Linkages	Biological Function or Location
Amylose			
Glycogen			
Chitin			
Cellulose			
Amylopectin			

Polysaccharide	Monosaccharide Units	Linkages	Biological Function or Location
Amylose	Glucose	$1,4\alpha$	Plant food storage
Glycogen	Glucose	$1,4\alpha$ and $1,6\alpha$	Animal food storage
Chitin	Glucosamine	$\beta 1,4$	Arthropod cuticle
Cellulose	Glucose (β)	$\beta 1,4$	Plant cell wall
Amylopectin	Glucose	$1,4\alpha$ and $1,6\alpha$	Plant food storage

Review: Unit 7, Items 13-22

8. Write the general formula for an amino acid.

$$R-\underset{\underset{NH_2}{|}}{\overset{\overset{H}{|}}{C}}-\underset{OH}{\overset{O}{C}}$$

Review: Unit 8, Items 1-3

9. List the seven classes of amino acids.

Hydrocarbon   Sulfur-Containing   Basic (Amino)
Hydroxy   Acid   Aromatic
Heterocyclic   *Review: Unit 8, Item 4*

10. Using the classes from your last answer, place the 21 common
    amino acids in the correct class. (Again, guess if you are not sure
    — do not ponder your answers long.)

Alanine	Isoleucine
Arginine	Leucine
Asparagine	Lysine
Aspartic Acid	Methionine
Cysteine	Phenylalanine
Cystine	Proline
Glutamic Acid	Serine
Glutamine	Threonine
Glycine	Tryptophan
Histidine	Tyrosine
	Valine

Hydrocarbon — glycine, alanine, valine, leucine, isoleucine (any
order)

Hydroxy — serine, threonine

Sulfur-Containing — cysteine, cystine, methionine

Acid — aspartic acid, glutamic acid

Basic — lysine, arginine, asparagine, glutamine

Aromatic — tyrosine, phenylalanine, tryptophan

Heterocyclic — tryptophan, histidine, proline

If you misplaced any of the amino acids, correct your response.

Review: Unit 8, Items 5-33

11. To which class of amino acids does each of the following belong?

Proline_____

Leucine_____

Lysine_____

Methionine_____

Tyrosine_____

Threonine_____

Cystine_____

- -

Proline Heterocyclic   Tyrosine Aromatic

Leucine Hydrocarbon   Threonine Hydroxy

Lycine Basic   Cystine Sulfur-containing

Methionine Sulfur-containing

---

12. Write the equation for the formation of a peptide bond between two amino acids of general structural formulae. Label the peptide bond.

- -

$$H-\underset{\underset{NH_2}{|}}{\overset{\overset{R}{|}}{C}}-C\overset{O}{\underset{OH}{\diagup}} \quad + \quad \underset{H}{\overset{H}{\diagdown}}N-\underset{\underset{H}{|}}{\overset{\overset{R}{|}}{C}}-C\overset{O}{\underset{OH}{\diagup}} \quad \rightleftharpoons \quad H-\underset{\underset{NH_2}{|}}{\overset{\overset{R}{|}}{C}}-\overset{\overset{O}{||}}{C}-N-\underset{\underset{H}{|}}{\overset{\overset{R}{|}}{C}}-C\overset{O}{\underset{OH}{\diagup}}$$

peptide bond

$$+ \ H_2O$$

13. Write the general structural formula for a pentapeptide. Circle each peptide unit.

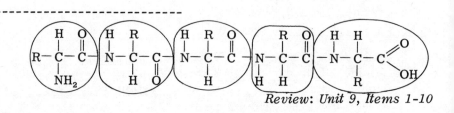

Review: Unit 9, Items 1-10

---

14. What is the approximate molecular weight range of proteins? What are the "building blocks" of proteins?

- -

5,000 to over a million (or approximate equivalent) amino acids (peptides)

Review: Unit 9, Item 11

---

15. Describe the α-helix structure. Who first postulated the structure of the α helix?

- -

The α helix-structure involves a coiling of the polypeptide chain which is stabilized by H bonding (H of −NH and =O of the carboxyl) between nearby units (3.7 units apart). The structure was postulated by Dr. Linus Pauling. (or similar responses)

Review: Unit 9, Items 17-22

16. What term is applied to each of the following?
   A. A protein made up of a polypeptide chain only.
   B. A protein made up of a polypeptide + a non-polypeptide group.
   C. The non-polypeptide group of "B."

   A. Simple protein   B. Conjugated protein   C. Prosthetic group
Review: *Unit 10, Items 18-19*

----

17. List and define briefly the four levels of protein structure. What types of bonding are involved in each?

   Primary structure — amino acid (peptide) sequence, peptide bond, S—S bonding of cystine.
   Secondary structure — bonding between nearby (5 units or less) peptides to produce a coiling or twisting in the backbone chain; for example, α helix. Stabilized by H bonding.
   Tertiary structure — bonding between distant peptides to cause the folding of a protein molecule. Types of bonding: hydrogen, hydrophobic, ionic, S—S bonds.
   Quaternary structure — bonding between subunits of a large protein; same types of bonding as tertiary structure.
   (or similar response)
Review: *Unit 10, Items 1-17*

----

18. Define a basic protein.

A basic protein contains a high percentage of lysine and arginine units (and asparagine and glutamine). (or similar response)
Review: Unit 10, Items 25-26

---

19. Define denaturation of a protein. What agents may cause denaturation?

Denaturation involves a change in the tertiary structure which causes a loss of biological activity. (or similar response) Agents: heat, organic solvents, acids, bases, etc. In general, agents which facilitate the disruption of H bonds. (or similar response)
Review: Unit 10, Items 21-24

Take at least a 5-minute break before continuing on to the next unit.

UNIT 11 *FATS, PHOSPHOLIPIDS, AND STEROLS*

Fats are important physiologically as food storage molecules and as thermal (heat) insulation in warm-blooded animals. You will construct and study the structural formula for a typical fat molecule. The related phospholipids are essential components of biological membranes. Using a fat molecule, you will modify it to form a phospholipid and will study the behavior and interaction of phospholipids in an aqueous medium. Another group of fat-like molecules, the sterols, function as membrane constituents, as hormones, and in fat digestion. The molecular structure of the sterols will also be studied and correlated with their biological function.

Material Covered

General structural formula of a fat
General structural formula of a phospholipid
Biological membrane structure
Sterols (steroid structure)
Biological functions of sterols

---

1. What two groups participate in an ester linkage?

- -

Carboxyl $\left(-C\overset{\displaystyle O}{\underset{\displaystyle OH}{}} \right)$ (organic acid)   (any order)

Hydroxyl ($-OH$)

---

2. Circle the hydroxyl groups.

$$
\begin{array}{c}
H \\
| \\
H-C-OH \\
| \\
H-C-OH \qquad \text{Glycerol} \\
| \\
H-C-OH \\
| \\
H
\end{array}
$$

- -

$$
\begin{array}{c}
H \\
| \\
H-C-\boxed{OH} \\
| \\
H-C-\boxed{OH} \\
| \\
H-C-\boxed{OH} \\
| \\
H
\end{array}
$$

---

3. Fatty Acids

$$
\begin{array}{cccc}
H & H \\
| & | \\
H-C-C-C{\nwarrow}^{O} \\
| & | & \searrow OH \\
H & H
\end{array}
\qquad\qquad
\begin{array}{ccccccc}
H & H & H & H & H & H & H \\
| & | & | & | & | & | & | \\
H-C-C-C-C-C-C-C-C{\nwarrow}^{O} \\
| & | & | & | & | & | & | & \searrow OH \\
H & H & H & H & H & H & H
\end{array}
$$

$$
\begin{array}{cccc}
H & H & H \\
| & | & | \\
H-C-C-C-C{\nwarrow}^{O} \\
| & | & | & \searrow OH \\
H & H & H
\end{array}
$$

Of what two groups is a fatty acid composed?

- -

Hydrocarbon
Carboxyl (organic acid)   (any order)

4. If the general formula for a fatty acid is: $R-C\overset{\displaystyle O}{\underset{\displaystyle OH}{\Big\backslash}}$, what does

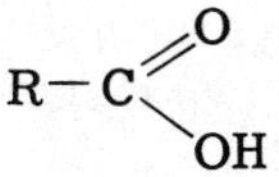

R equal?

- -

R = a hydrocarbon group

---

5. Form an ester linkage between the *top* C of glycerol and the fatty acid

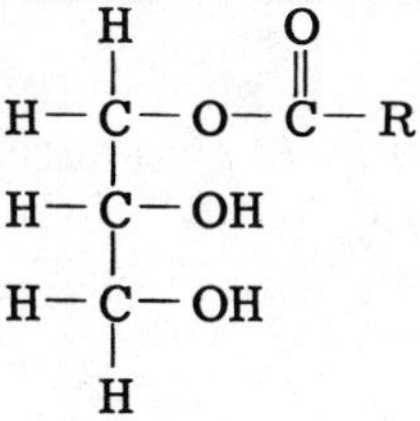

$$
\begin{array}{c}
\text{H} \\
| \\
\text{H}-\text{C}-\text{OH} \\
| \\
\text{H}-\text{C}-\text{OH} \\
| \\
\text{H}-\text{C}-\text{OH} \\
| \\
\text{H}
\end{array}
\qquad\qquad
R-C\overset{\displaystyle O}{\underset{\displaystyle OH}{\Big\backslash}}
$$

- -

$$
\begin{array}{c}
\text{H} \quad\quad \text{O} \\
| \quad\quad\ \ \| \\
\text{H}-\text{C}-\text{O}-\text{C}-\text{R} \\
| \\
\text{H}-\text{C}-\text{OH} \\
| \\
\text{H}-\text{C}-\text{OH} \\
| \\
\text{H}
\end{array}
$$

---

6. Similarly, form ester linkages with the remaining two C's of glycerol and two more molecules of fatty acid.

- -

$$
\begin{array}{c}
\text{H} \quad\quad \text{O} \\
| \qquad\quad \parallel \\
\text{H}-\text{C}-\text{O}-\text{C}-\text{R} \\
| \\
\quad\quad\quad \text{O} \\
\quad\quad\quad \parallel \\
\text{H}-\text{C}-\text{O}-\text{C}-\text{R} \\
| \\
\quad\quad\quad \text{O} \\
\quad\quad\quad \parallel \\
\text{H}-\text{C}-\text{O}-\text{C}-\text{R} \\
| \\
\text{H}
\end{array}
$$

7. You have just constructed a *fat* (or biological oil). In the "R" of fats, C = 15 or 17 (usually). Write out the *complete* structural formula for a fat made up of stearic acid ($C_{17}H_{35}COOH$). (All fats contain glycerol.)

- -

8. Look carefully at the fat you have just diagrammed. Would you expect this fat to be soluble in water? Explain your answer.

No. The hydrophobic groups (nonpolar or hydrocarbon groups) promote insolubility. (or similar answer)

9. Which of the following would be the *least* soluble in H_2O?
   A. $C_{21}H_{43}COOH$
   B. $C_{17}H_{35}COOH$
   C. $C_5H_{11}COOH$

A

10. Would several fat molecules cluster together in water? Explain your answer.

Yes. Hydrophobic bonding (hydrophobic groups tend to cluster together).

11. Diagram the structure of a fat composed of: $C_{17}H_{33}C\overset{\displaystyle O}{\underset{\displaystyle OH}{\Big\langle}}$ (oleic acid) using the empirical formula. Oleic acid contains a double bond: in the middle of the carbon chain, e.g.

$$-\overset{\displaystyle H}{\underset{\displaystyle H}{\overset{|}{\underset{|}{C}}}}-\overset{}{\underset{\displaystyle H}{\overset{}{\underset{|}{C}}}}=\overset{}{\underset{\displaystyle H}{\overset{}{\underset{|}{C}}}}-\overset{\displaystyle H}{\underset{\displaystyle H}{\overset{|}{\underset{|}{C}}}}-$$

- -

$$H-\overset{\displaystyle H}{\underset{\displaystyle |}{\overset{|}{C}}}-O-\overset{\displaystyle O}{\overset{\|}{C}}-C_{17}H_{33}$$

$$\overset{\displaystyle |}{} \qquad \overset{\displaystyle O}{\overset{\|}{}}$$

$$H-\overset{|}{\underset{|}{C}}-O-\overset{\|}{C}-C_{17}H_{33}$$

$$\overset{\displaystyle |}{} \qquad \overset{\displaystyle O}{\overset{\|}{}}$$

$$H-\overset{|}{\underset{\displaystyle H}{\overset{|}{C}}}-O-\overset{\|}{C}-C_{17}H_{33}$$

12.

$$H-\overset{\overset{\displaystyle H}{|}}{C}-O-\overset{\overset{\displaystyle O}{\parallel}}{C}-C_{17}H_{35}$$

$$H-\overset{|}{C}-O-\overset{\overset{\displaystyle O}{\parallel}}{C}-C_{17}H_{35}$$

$$H-\overset{\overset{|}{C}}{\underset{\overset{|}{H}}{}}-O-\overset{\overset{\displaystyle O}{\parallel}}{\underset{\overset{|}{OH}}{P}}-O-R_S$$

This is the structural formula of a typical *phospholipid*. What two groups of the phospholipid replace one of the fatty acids in its related fat?

- -

$$O-\overset{\overset{\displaystyle O}{\parallel}}{\underset{\overset{|}{OH}}{P}}-O- \quad \text{(phosphate)}$$

R_S (R_S = a water soluble group)

---

13. In the phospholipid lecithin the R_S group is:

$$-\overset{\overset{\displaystyle H}{|}}{\underset{\overset{|}{H}}{C}}-\overset{\overset{\displaystyle H}{|}}{\underset{\overset{|}{H}}{C}}-\overset{\overset{\displaystyle CH_3}{|}}{\underset{\overset{|}{CH_3}}{N}}\overset{\oplus}{=}CH_3$$

Is this R_S group a part of an ion? Would this R_S group promote solubility in water? Explain your answer.

- -

Yes (+ charge)
Yes (it would attract water molecules due to the + charge)

---

14. On the diagram of the phospholipid (item 12) circle and label the
portions of the molecule which are *hydrophobic* (water hating).
Also circle and label the portions of the molecule which are
hydrophylic (water loving).

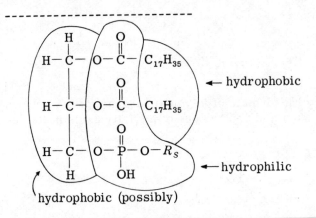

R_s

← hydrophobic

← hydrophilic

hydrophobic (possibly)

15. Diagram the general structure of a phospholipid. Use

$$R_f - C \underset{\text{OH}}{\overset{O}{\diagup}} = \text{the fatty acids}$$

R_s = the H_2O soluble group

$$\begin{array}{l}
\quad\;\; H \quad\;\; O \\
\quad\;\; | \quad\quad \| \\
H - C - O - C - R_f \\
\quad\;\; | \\
\quad\quad\quad\;\; O \\
\quad\quad\quad\;\; \| \\
H - C - O - C - R_f \quad (\text{or similar structures}) \\
\quad\;\; | \\
\quad\quad\quad\;\; O \\
\quad\quad\quad\;\; \| \\
H - C - O - P - O - R_s \\
\quad\;\; | \quad\quad | \\
\quad\;\; H \quad\;\; OH
\end{array}$$

16. Phospholipids are frequently written in ultrashorthand form thus:

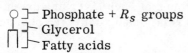

Label the hydrophobic groups and the hydrophylic group on the shorthand diagram.

- -

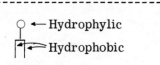

---

17. Diagram five (shorthand form) phospholipid molecules to indicate the clustering together of the hydrophobic groups in water.

- -

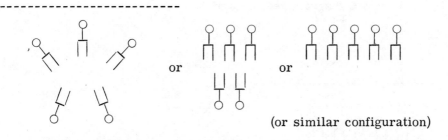

(or similar configuration)

---

18. Write the shorthand form of a phospholipid molecule and label the hydrocarbon and water-soluble groups.

- -

Q ←— Water soluble groups

←=Hydrocarbon groups

---

19. Biological membranes are composed of two layers of phospholipid molecules. The hydrophobic groups of each layer are oriented (pointed) inward. Diagram this relationship using ten shorthand form phospholipid molecules.

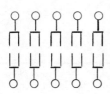

20. In biological membranes, both *outer surfaces* of the phospholipid layer are covered with layers of protein. Use ⋁⋁⋁⋁⋁⋁ = a polypeptide chain (protein). Add protein to the phospholipid double layer you diagrammed in item 19.

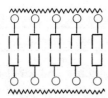

21. Recall the properties of proteins. Label the *hydrophobic* and
    hydrophylic portions of the membrane diagram.

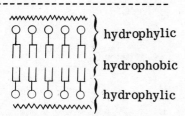

22. Diagram the basic structure of a biological membrane. Label the
    two major components (type of chemical compound involved).

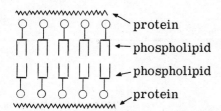

23. Steroid Nucleus

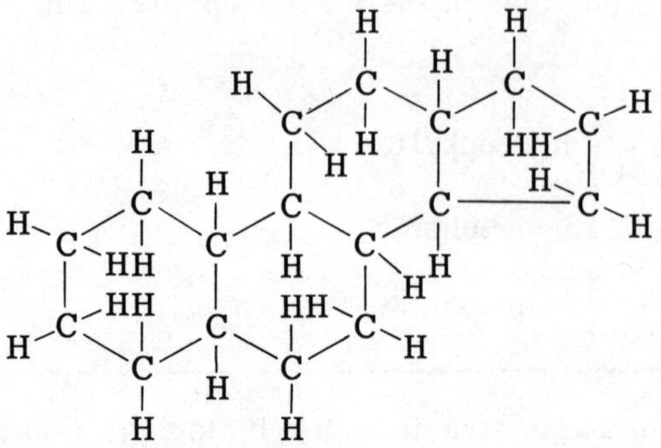

Is this steroid aromatic? In what chemical group would you place this steroid? Would it be hydrophylic or hydrophobic?

No
Hydrocarbon (cyclic)
Hydrophobic

24.

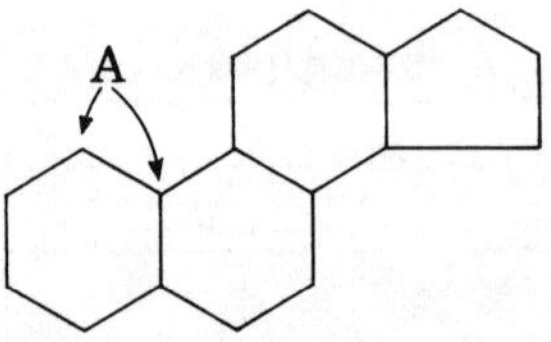

The steroid nucleus (basic ring structure) can also be diagrammed in this shorthand fashion. What atom is located at each intersection or point? (arrows) Ⓐ

C (carbon)

25. Each C atom is assigned a number.

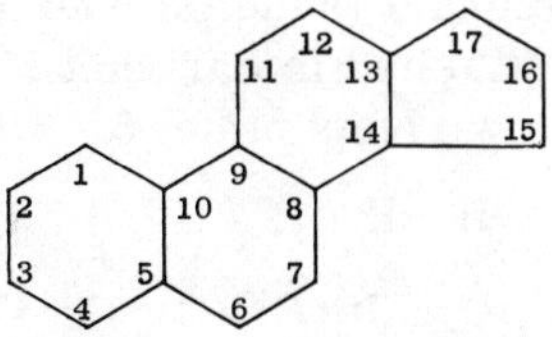

How many H's are bonded to carbon #1?   5?   17?

4?   8?   15?

#1. 2 H   5. 1 H   17. 2 H
 4. 2 H   8. 1 H   15. 2 H

---

26. A ster*ol* (as contrasted to a ster*oid*) has one or more OH groups in the molecule. For example, cholesterol (liver bile), a sterol which functions in emulsification of fat, has an − OH group on carbon #3. Refer to item 25 and diagram a shorthand steroid nucleus with this OH added.

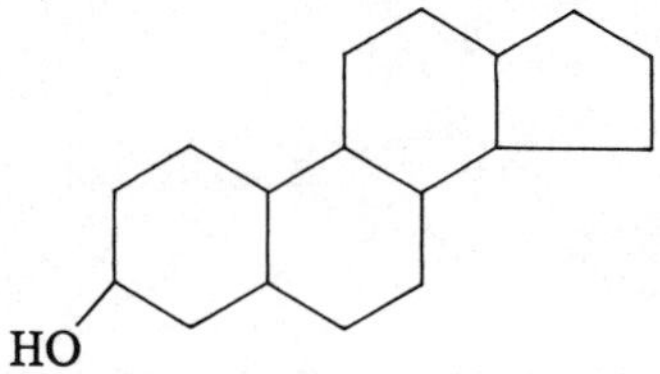

HO

27. In cholesterol, there are also other differences from the basic steroid nucleus. Diagram these on your outline diagram (item 26). Methyl groups are attached to carbons 10 and 13. There is a double bond between carbons 5 and 6. A hydrocarbon chain

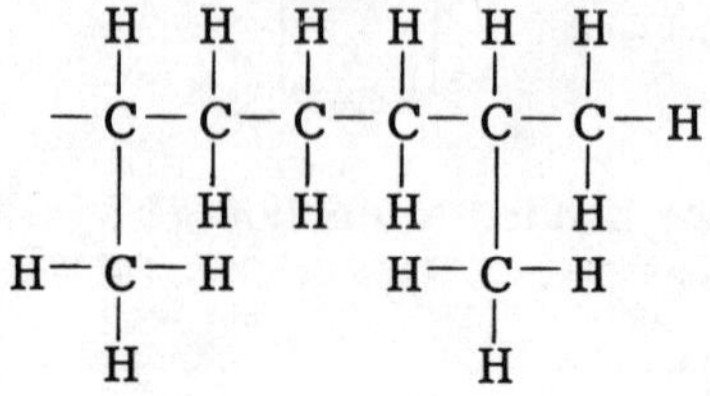

is attached to carbon #17.

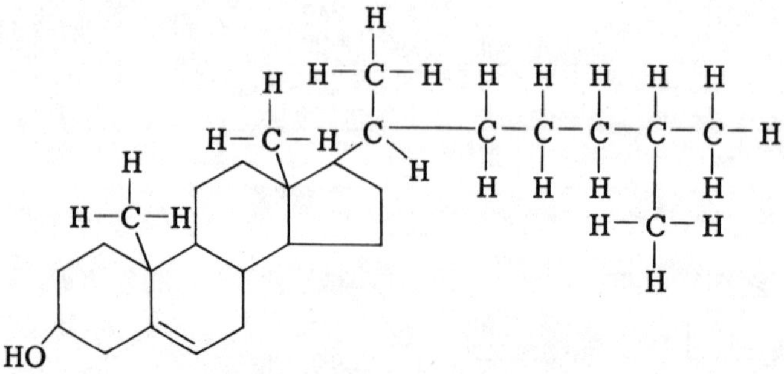

---

28. Which portion of the cholesterol molecule would be *hydrophylic*? Sterols are a common constituent of biological membranes. Would you expect to find them in the lipid or protein layer?

−OH
Lipid (due to hydrophobic bonding)

29. Diagram the basic ring structure of a steroid.

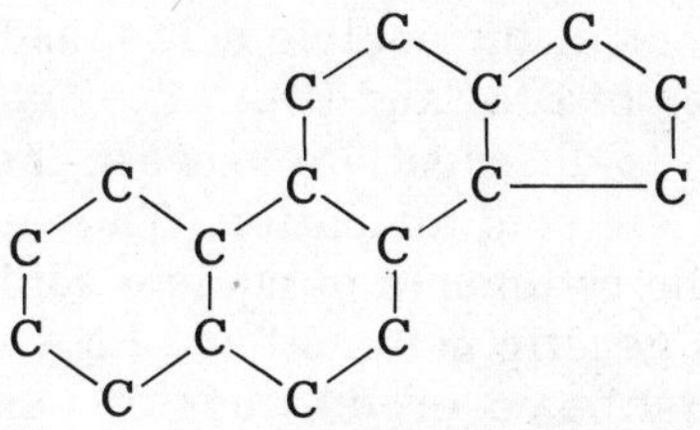

or

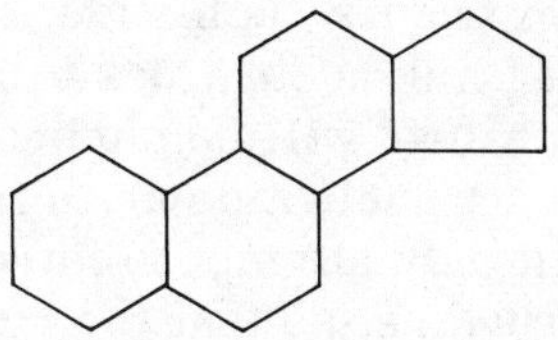

---

30. The sex hormones, androgens in the male and estrogens and pro-
gesterone in the female, and the hormones of the adrenal cortex,
are sterols, List the two other basic functions of the sterols we
have discussed.

Cholesterol — liver bile sterol which functions in emulsification
  of fats.
Constituents of membrane structure.

---

31. What are three major biological functions of sterols?

As hormones, membrane structure, and bile sterol (cholesterol).

Take at least a 5-minute break before continuing to the next unit.

UNIT *12* *NUCLEIC ACIDS*

The nucleic acids function in living organisms as genetic material and in the control of protein (hence enzyme) synthesis. You will first construct a nucleotide, the building block of the nucleic acids, and will then link nucleotides to form molecules of DNA and RNA. The "genetic alphabet" will be studied, as you learn to differentiate between the different nucleotide units involved in nucleic acid formation. This unit will only attempt to introduce you to the rudiments of nucleic acid structure, so that the roles of DNA as genetic material and RNA as the machinery of protein synthesis must be covered by use of a supplementary text or lecture.

Related polyphosphate molecules (ATP, etc.) function in energy transfer within organisms. Since ATP is essentially a nucleotide, its structural formula will also be studied.

Material Covered

Purines, pyrimidines
Nucleotides
Deoxyribose nucleic acid (DNA) structure
Base pairing in DNA
Ribose nucleic acid (RNA) structure
ATP — structure and function
Basic protein — nucleic acid bonding

1.

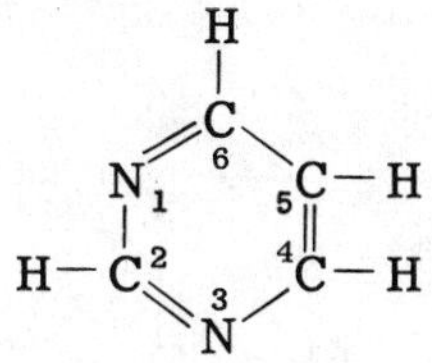

Pyrimidine ring

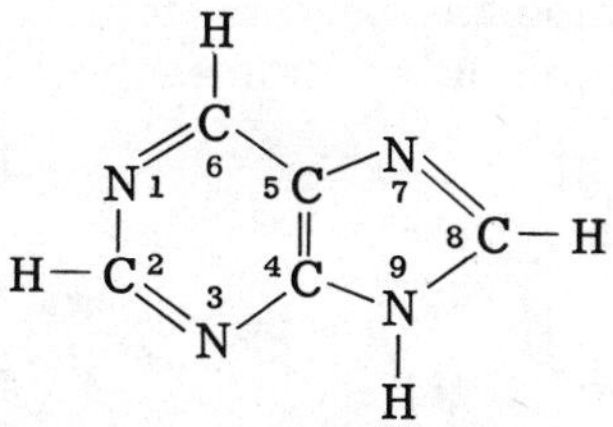

Purine ring

Write a shorthand diagram for the two nitrogen bases, the purine and pyrimidine rings. (Remember that *only* C and H are *not* written in a shorthand diagram.)

- -

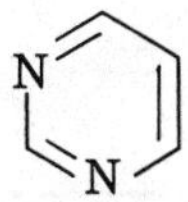

Pyrimidine (one ring)

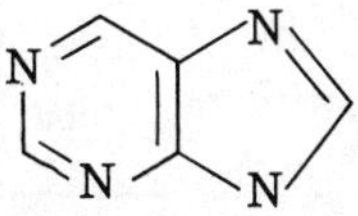

Purine (two rings)
(Pu-rymes with two)

2. Without looking back to item 1, label each of the following N-bases as a purine or pyrimidine.

Adenine

Uracil

Thymine

Guanine

Cytosine

- -

Adenine — purine   Guanine — purine
Uracil — pyrimidine   Cytosine — pyrimidine
Thymine — pyrimidine   (memorize this list)

---

3. Label each of the following N-bases as a purine or pyrimidine.
   Adenine   Thymine
   Cytosine   Uracil
   Guanine

- -

Adenine — purine   Thymine — pyrimidine
Cytosine — pyrimidine   Uracil — pyrimidine
Guanine — purine

---

4. In Unit 7 on carbohydrates, you learned the structural formula for two pentoses. What were these two pentoses? (If you cannot re-call, see item 1, Unit 7.)

- -

Deoxyribose ⎫ any order
Ribose   ⎭

5. Write the structural formulae for ribose and deoxyribose. Number the C atoms of one molecule. (If you do not remember, guess.)

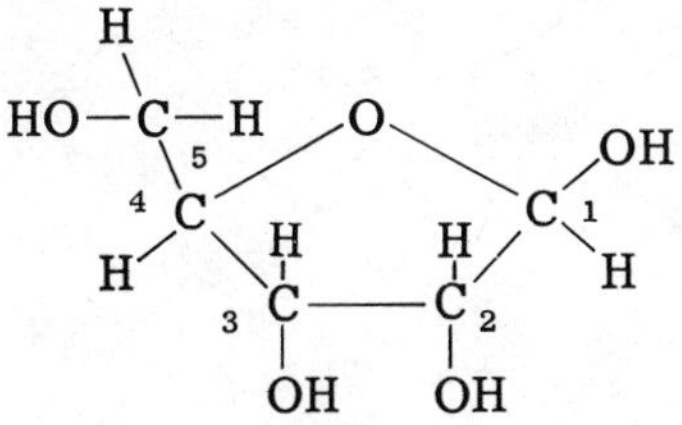

Ribose

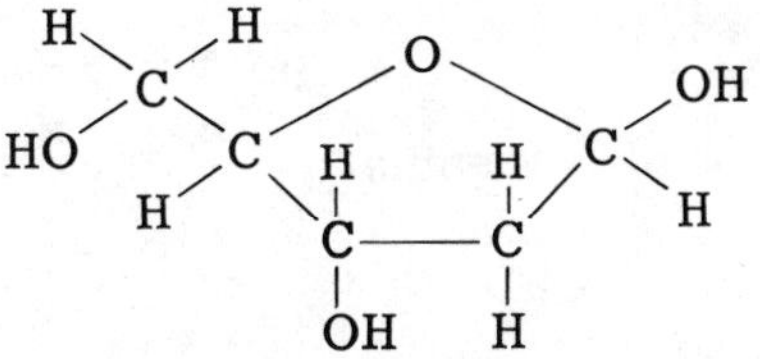

Deoxyribose
(Check numbers carefully)

6. Write the structural formula for ribose in the mirror image form (C #1 on the left and C #5 on the right).

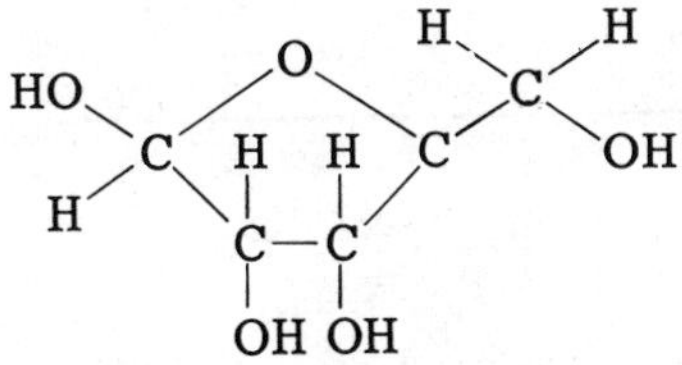

7. Attach a molecule of ribose (in the mirror image form) to this molecule of adenine by a covalent bond between atom #9 of the adenine (see item 1) and C #1 of the ribose. What molecule is split out in the formation of this covalent bond?

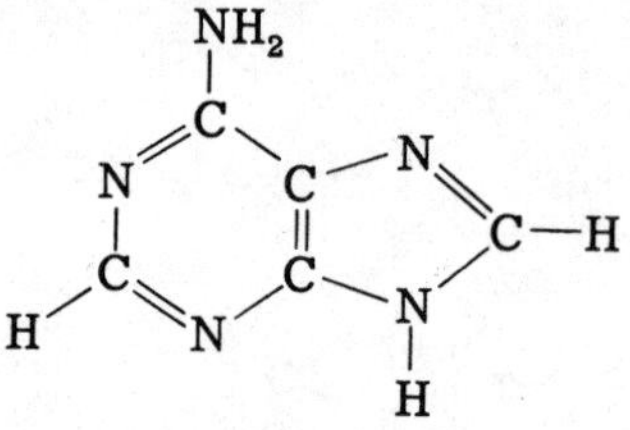

Adenine

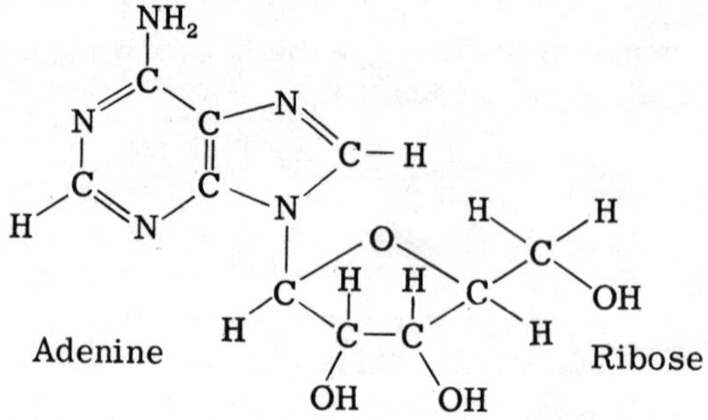

Adenine   Ribose

Water is split out.

8. To the molecule you diagrammed in the previous item, add a phosphate group via an *ester linkage* to C #5 of the ribose component. (This type of ester linkage will be referred to as a phosphate ester linkage since it involves phosphorous rather than a carbon atom.)

(This molecule is a *nucleotide, adenosine monophosphate*)

9. In similar fashion the other N-bases, cytosine, guanine, thymine, and uracil will form nucleotides. Also, the other pentose sugar, deoxyribose, can form nucleotides. In this nucleotide, circle and label the three basic components.

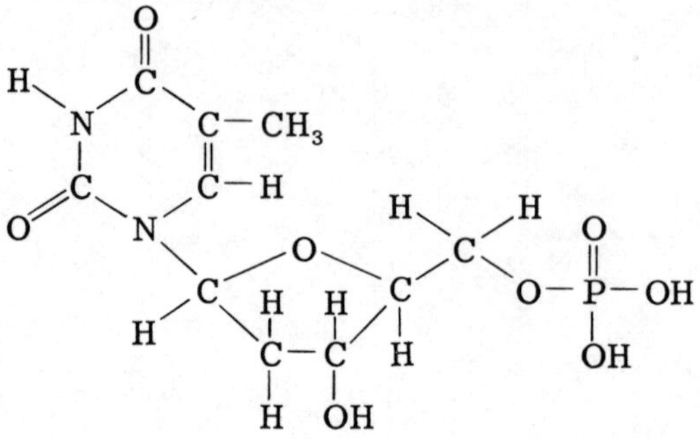

- -

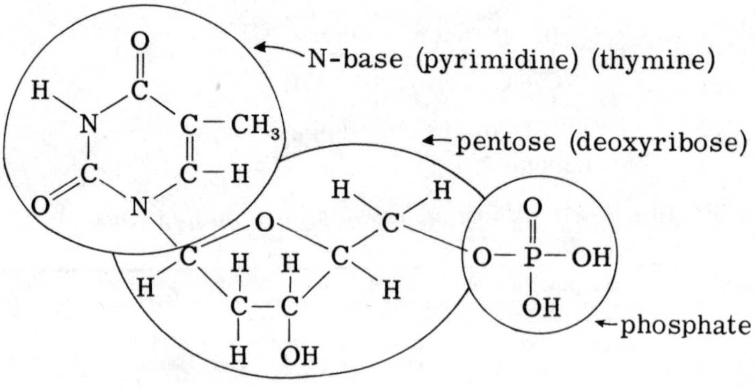

N-base (pyrimidine) (thymine)

pentose (deoxyribose)

phosphate

---

10. What are the three components of which a nucleotide is composed?

- -

N-base (purine or pyrimidine)
Pentose sugar (ribose or deoxyribose)
Phosphate
(any order)

---

11. Diagram the *shorthand* structural formula for the nucleotide, adenosine monophosphate. Use the shorthand diagram for adenine =:

----

12. Two nucleotides can be linked together by a phosphate ester linkage between the P of one nucleotide and sugar C #3 of the other nucleotide. Diagram this linkage. Diagram only the phosphate group of one nucleotide and the deoxyribose of the other.

(or other reasonable forms of the same ester linkage)

13. A nucleotide can be written in (ultra) shorthand form:

P— R
  | = Adenosine monophosphate
  A

Write the shorthand form for thymidine monophosphate. What
does R stand for ? What would D stand for ?

P— R
  |
  T
Ribose
Deoxyribose

---

14. When two nucleotides are linked together, between which two components is the phosphate ester linkage formed? Using the ultrashorthand forms, diagram a dinucleotide between adenosine monophosphate and guanidine monophosphate (use D in both nucleotides.)

P and (D or R)

P— D— P— D
  | |
  A   G

---

15. Write a shorthand form diagram of a chain or 5 nucleotides (aden-
    osine monophosphate (AMP), cytidine monophosphate (CMP), GMP,
    AMP, and TMP) use:

    P = Phosphate   A = adenine   G = guanine
    D = Deoxyribose   T = thymine   C = cytosine
    Circle each nucleotide.

- -

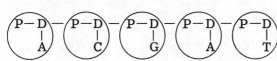

You have diagrammed a short segment of *deoxyribose nucleic acid
— DNA*. *Genes* are constituted of *DNA*.

---

16. In deoxyribose nucleic acid (DNA), the pentose sugar is always
    _____? DNA is composed of four types of
    nucleotides, each containing the N base adenine or cytosine or
    guanine or thymine. Which of these N bases are purines and which
    are pyrimidines?

- -

Deoxyribose
Adenine $\Big\}$ purines   Thymine $\Big\}$ pyrimidines
Guanine   Cytosine

---

17. Write the shorthand form for a DNA strand containing the follow-
    ing sequence of six nucleotides: GMP, CMP, TMP, CMP, AMP,
    TMP.

- -

```
P—D— P— D— P— D— P— D— P— D— P— D
   |      |      |      |      |      |
   G      C      T      C      A      T
```

Note: the P— D— P— D etc. chain is frequently called the *backbone*.

---

18. The DNA molecule consists of two strands of DNA which are linked by H-bonding between the N-bases: (A and T) and (G and C), thus:

Strand 1 ⟶ P—D—P—D—P—D—P—D—P—D—P—D
      | | | | | |
      G   C   T   C   A   T

         C   G   A
         | | |
Strand 2 ⟶ P—D—P—D—P—D

Complete strand 2. Label the backbone of each strand.

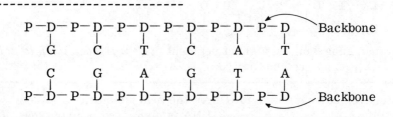

19. List the four N-bases which occur in DNA. Indicate the N-base pairing which occurs in DNA structure.

Adenine ⎫
Thymine ⎭ pair   Cytosine ⎫
         Guanine ⎭ pair

(Note that the C and G, which look alike, pair.)

20. Write in the H bonds which could form between thymine and adenine.

Thymine

$-\text{(D)}$ = deoxyribose   Adenine

- -

Thymine   Adenine

These two H bonds are responsible for A—T pairing. Remember that the H of C—H (circle) does *not* form H bonds.

21. Write in the H bonds which could form between cytosine and guanine.

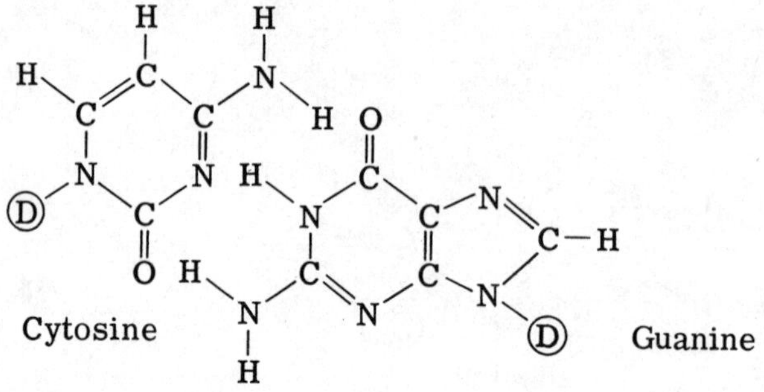

Cytosine   Guanine

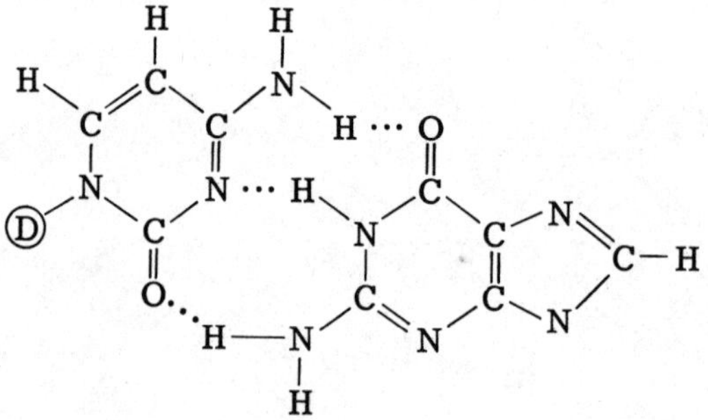

These three H bonds are responsible for C—G pairing.

---

22. How many H bonds are formed between each of the following N-base pairs?

A—T _____   G—C _____

A—T _____2_____ (A:::T) G—C _____3_____ (G:::C)

23. Write the complementary half of this DNA chain. Include all H
bonds (:::) or (::). Circle each nucleotide in the entire molecule.

```
P— D— P— D— P— D— P— D— P— D— P— D
    |       |       |       |       |       |
    C       G       C       A       C       T
```

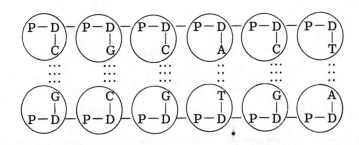

---

24. This double stranded "ladder-like" structure of DNA was first
postulated by Watson and Crick in 1953 on the basis of x-ray dif-
fraction analysis. The two strands are also coiled in a helical
form. Thus, the molecular structure of DNA is referred to as the
Watson-Crick double helix. (Memorize this term.) Models and
diagrams of this structure can be seen in most biology and genetics texts by consulting the index. If you have a text available
look up the structure now; then go on to the next item.

25. RNA = *ribose nucleic acid*. T does not occur in RNA (T is replaced by U = uracil). Write the *RNA* complement to this *DNA*
strand. Include all H bonds.

```
P— D— P— D— P— D— P— D— P— D— P— D ◄—DNA strand
    |       |       |       |       |       |
    A       T       C       A       T       G
```

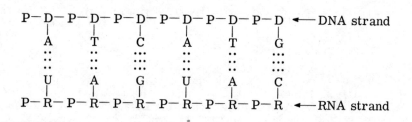

```
P— D— P— D— P— D— P— D— P— D— P— D  ◄— DNA strand
    |       |       |       |       |       |
    A       T       C       A       T       G
    ::      ::      :::     ::      ::      :::
    ::      ::      :::     ::      ::      :::
    ::      ::      :::     ::      ::      :::
    U       A       G       U       A       C
    |       |       |       |       |       |
P— R— P— R— P— R— P— R— P— R— P— R  ◄—RNA strand
```

26. RNA *does not* (usually) form a double-stranded helix. RNA can
be manufactured in the cell from genetic DNA. Construct the
RNA complement to this genetic DNA strand. Circle each nucleotide.

```
P— D— P— D— P— D— P— D— P— D— P— D— P— D
    |       |       |       |       |       |       |
    A       T       G       A       C       C       T
```

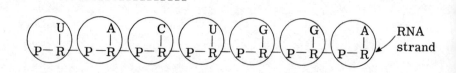

RNA strand

27. List three differences between DNA and RNA.

- -

1. Uracil (RNA) replaces thymine (DNA)
2. Ribose (RNA) replaces deoxyribose (DNA)
3. DNA usually occurs in the *double stranded helix.* RNA is usually *single stranded.*
(or similar responses) (any order)

28. What name is applied to the model for the molecular structure of DNA?

- -

Watson-Crick double helix.

29. Complete this structure formula for adenine:

- -

30. Write the structural formula for adenine. (Do not consult the previous items.)

- -

$$
\begin{array}{c}
\text{NH}_2 \\
\mid \\
\text{C} \\
\text{N} \quad \text{C} - \text{N} \\
\parallel \quad\quad \parallel \quad\quad \text{C} - \text{H} \\
\text{C} \quad \text{C} \quad \text{N} \\
\text{H} \quad \text{N} \quad\quad \mid \\
\text{H}
\end{array}
$$

31. Use your previous structural formula for adenine; add to it to diagram the structural formula for adenosine monophosphate (ribose form).

- -

$$
\begin{array}{c}
\text{NH}_2 \\
\mid \\
\text{C} \\
\text{N} \quad \text{C} - \text{N} \\
\parallel \quad\quad \parallel \quad \text{C} - \text{H} \\
\text{C} \quad \text{C} \quad \text{N} \\
\text{H} \quad \text{N} \quad\quad \\
\end{array}
$$

Adenosine monophosphate (AMP)

32. Use the previous structural formula for adenosine monophosphate and add a second phosphate group via an ester linkage to the first phosphate. What other (small) molecule is produced when this linkage is formed?

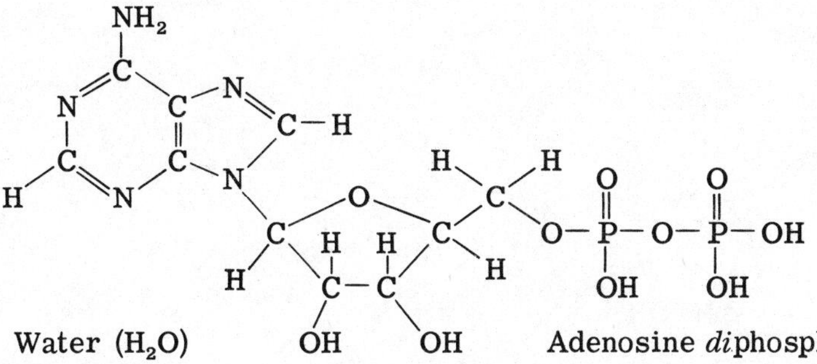

NH₂

Water (H₂O)   OH   OH   Adenosine *di*phosphate (ADP)

33. Use the previous structural formula for adenosine diphosphate and add a third phosphate group via an ester linkage to the second phosphate. What is the name of this molecule? What abbreviation would be used for it?

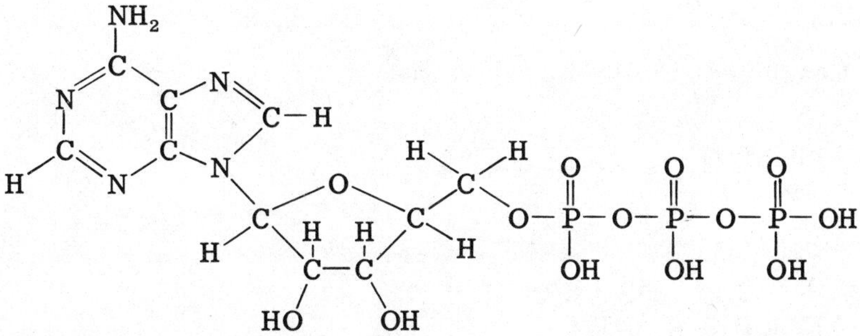

NH₂

Adenosine triphosphate (ATP)
ATP functions in cellular energy transfer.

34. Write the shorthand structural formula for ATP. What is the chief function of ATP?

ATP functions in biological energy transfer.

---

35. Complete the following equation:

ADP + P ⇌ _____ + H_2O

ADP + P ⇌ ATP + H_2O

---

36. Complete the following equations:

AMP + P ⇌ _____ + _____
ATP + H_2O ⇌ _____ + P
AMP + 2P ⇌ _____ + _____

AMP + P ⇌ ADP + H_2O
ATP + H_2O ⇌ ADP + P
AMP + 2P ⇌ ATP + $2H_2O$

37. What is the chief characteristic of a basic protein? (If you do not remember for sure, guess.)

A basic protein contains a high proportion of the basic (NH_2) amino acids, lysine and arginine. (or similar response)

---

38. What groups would be particularly involved in the H bonding between a basic protein and the *backbone* of a nucleic acid?

Protein: H from NH_2 groups

Nucleic acids: $=O$ from $-\overset{\overset{\displaystyle O}{\|}}{\underset{\underset{\displaystyle OH}{|}}{P}}-$

---

39. What are the structural units of the nucleic acids?

Nucleotides

---

40. Write out the full name for DNA and RNA.

DNA = deoxyribosenucleic acid
RNA = ribose nucleic acid

Take at least a 5-minute break before continuing on to the next unit.

One of the fundamental properties of living systems is their ability to transform energy. We shall deal with the energy changes that accompany biological reactions in a simplified way, attempting to relate chemical changes to energy changes. The role of enzymes in biochemical reactions will also be related to energetic considerations, and the binding of molecules to the enzyme surface during a reaction will be diagrammed.

Energy transformations are among the most important and most difficult concepts to learn in beginning biology. Especially careful thought will be desirable in approaching this unit.

Material Covered

Potential vs. kinetic energy
calories and Calories
Bond energy
Exothermic and endothermic reactions
Energy of activation
Concentration of reactants and products at equilibrium
Catalysts
Enzymes
Bonds involved in enzyme-substrate complex.

1. Label each of the following as an example of either *potential
    energy* or *kinetic energy*:
    A. A landslide
    B. Balancing rock.
    C. Water (spilling) over the dam.
    D. Molecular motion.
    E. The lake of water behind the dam.
    F. The energy of a covalent bond.
    G. Hot coffee (as opposed to cold coffee).

    A. Kinetic
    B. Potential
    C. Kinetic
    D. Kinetic
    E. Potential
    F. Potential
    G. Kinetic ("heat" is increased molecular motion)

---

2. Define briefly potential energy and kinetic energy.

    Potential energy is restrained energy which can be available to do
    work upon removal of the restraint. (e.g., water behind the dam)
    Kinetic energy is the energy of motion. (e.g., molecular motion)

---

3. Persons who are overweight are sometimes concerned about the
    energy content of their diet. In what units do they usually count
    the energy content of foods?

    Calories

---

4. Thus, the biologist would write:

    Glucose + $6O_2 \rightleftharpoons 6CO_2 + 6H_2O + 673$____?____(units of energy)

    Calories

---

5. In a closed system (e.g., a thermos bottle) it takes:
   250 calories of heat to raise 250 ml H_2O 1°C.
   37 calories of heat to raise   1 ml H_2O 37°C.
   100 calories of heat to raise 10 ml H_2O 10°C.
   Define a calorie.

A calorie is the amount of heat required to raise 1 ml H_2O 1°C.
(or similar response)

---

6. 1 Calorie = 1 Kilo calorie = 1000 calories
   How many Calories does 3000 calories equal?
   How many calories does 132 Calories equal?
   How many Calories does 132 calories equal?

----

   3   132,000   0.132 $\left(\dfrac{132}{1000}\right)$

---

7. Which of the following molecules would you expect to contain the greatest potential energy?

A. $H-\overset{\overset{\displaystyle H}{|}}{\underset{\underset{\displaystyle H}{|}}{C}}-C\overset{\displaystyle O}{\underset{\displaystyle OH}{\big<}}$

B. $H-\overset{\overset{\displaystyle H}{|}}{\underset{\underset{\displaystyle H}{|}}{C}}-\overset{\overset{\displaystyle H}{|}}{\underset{\underset{\displaystyle H}{|}}{C}}-\overset{\overset{\displaystyle H}{|}}{\underset{\underset{\displaystyle H}{|}}{C}}-\overset{\overset{\displaystyle H}{|}}{\underset{\underset{\displaystyle H}{|}}{C}}-C\overset{\displaystyle O}{\underset{\displaystyle OH}{\big<}}$

C. $H-\overset{\overset{\displaystyle H}{|}}{\underset{\underset{\displaystyle NH_2}{|}}{C}}-C\overset{\displaystyle O}{\underset{\displaystyle OH}{\big<}}$

Explain your answer.

B, because B contains the greatest number of bonds.

8. Given:

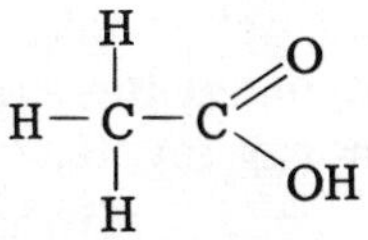

$$\underset{\underset{\text{H}}{|}}{\overset{\overset{\text{H}}{|}}{\text{H}-\text{C}-\text{C}}} \overset{O}{\underset{OH}{\diagdown}} + 2O_2 \rightleftharpoons 2CO_2 + 2H_2O + \text{Energy}$$

$6CO_2 + 6H_2O + \text{Energy} \rightleftharpoons \text{Glucose} + 6O_2$

Pyruvic Acid $\rightleftharpoons$ Acetic acid $+ CO_2 + $ Energy

In general: Is energy consumed or released as a large molecule is formed? Is energy consumed or released as a large molecule is broken down?

- -

Formed — energy is consumed
Broken — energy is released

---

9. An *exothermic* reaction: Glucose $+ 6O_2 \rightleftharpoons 6CO_2 + 6H_2O + $ Energy
An *endothermic* reaction: $6CO_2 + 6H_2O + $ Energy $\rightleftharpoons$ Glucose $+ 6O_2$

From what you can reason out about the word meanings, define an exothermic and an endothermic reaction.

- -

An *exothermic* reaction *releases* energy (heat).
An *endothermic* reaction *consumes* energy.
(or similar responses)

---

10. Label each of the following reactions as either exothermic or endothermic. (If you are in doubt check back to Item No. 8.)
    A. Pyruvic acid $+ 3O_2 \rightleftharpoons 3CO_2 + 3H_2O$
    B. $C_4H_6O_4 \rightleftharpoons C_4H_4O_4 + 2(H)$
    C. Amino acids $\rightleftharpoons$ Polypeptide chain (Protein)
    D. ADP $+ P \rightleftharpoons$ ATP
    E. Glycerol $+ 3$ Fatty acids $\rightleftharpoons$ Fat

- -

A. Exothermic   D. Endothermic
B. Exothermic   E. Endothermic
C. Endothermic

---

11. In a collection of molecules, for example, let us take a solution of ATP in water, all molecules are not moving at the same rate; therefore, they have different kinetic energy levels. This can be illustrated by the plot:

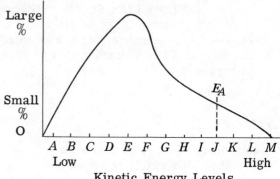

Which *energy level* is higher (D or G)? Which energy level contains the greatest number of molecules of ATP (D or G)? Would the number of molecules of ATP at energy level J or higher be relatively large or small?

- -

G (A is low; M is high)
D
Small

---

12. In order for two molecules to combine, they must come together or collide. Which would facilitate collisions, a high or low kinetic energy? In the reaction $ATP + H_2O \rightleftharpoons ADP + Ph + 10$ Cal., which two molecules must collide for ADP and Ph to be produced?

- -

A high kinetic energy (will facilitate collisions)
$ATP + H_2O$

13. Not all molecules of ATP and H_2O which collide can react. In the reaction ATP + H_2O ⇌ ADP + Ph + 10 Cal., an ester linkage between the second Ph and the third Ph of ATP must be broken if the reaction goes to the right. Only a few colliding molecules of ATP and H_2O have enough kinetic energy to allow this bond (of the ester linkage) to be broken. This energy level is called the energy of activation. In the plot of item 11, the energy of activation (E_A) is labeled. Is the proportion of molecules which have a kinetic energy level above E_A large or small? In your own words, define the energy of activation.

Small
The energy of activation is the minimum energy level which two colliding molecules must possess in order to undergo a given chemical reaction. (or similar response)

_____

14. Given the reaction: ATP + H_2O ⇌ ADP + Ph + 10 Cal., the following relationship holds:

Energy level scale

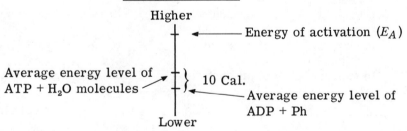

For which reaction (right or left) is the activation energy the greatest? Which group of molecules (ATP + H_2O or ADP + Ph) would you then expect to have the greatest proportion of molecules at a kinetic energy level above E_A ?

Left (ADP + Ph are the reactants)
ATP + H_2O

_____

15. Define chemical equilibrium for the reaction:
$$ATP + H_2O \rightleftharpoons ADP + P + 10 \text{ Cal.}$$

At equilibrium, rate to the right = rate to left.

---

16. If ATP is added to the reaction at equilibrium, what will be the initial effect on the rate of the reaction to the right?

In general:
An increase in the concentration of the reactants will cause a(n) _____ in the rate of the reaction to the right.
An increase in the concentration of the products will cause a(n) _____ in the rate of the reaction to the left.
A decrease in the concentration of the reactants will cause a(n) _____ in the rate of the reaction to the right.
A decrease in the concentration of the products will cause a(n) _____ in the rate of the reaction to the left.

Rate would increase.
↑ in concentration of reactants → ⌈ ↑ ⌉ in rate of reaction to
   right
↑ in concentration of products → | ↑ | in rate of reaction to
   left.
↓ in concentration of reactants → | ↓ | in rate of reaction to
   right.
↓ in concentration of products → ⌊ ↓ ⌋ in rate of reaction to
   left.

---

17. The rate of a reaction is determined by the number of molecules which are at an energy level above the energy of activation. At equilibrium, what relationship must be true for the number of molecule pairs of $ATP + H_2O$ and $ADP + Ph$ which are above E_A?

$(ATP + H_2O) = (ADP + Ph)$ (i.e. the rate to the right = the rate to the left.)

---

18. ATP + H_2O ⇌ ADP + Ph + 10 Cal.   If the reaction to the left has a
    higher energy of activation than the reaction to the right (see
    item 14), will a higher or lower concentration of ADP + P (as
    compared to the concentration of ATP + H_2O) be present at
    equilibrium?

    Higher (The higher the E_A the lower the proportion of molecules
    above E_A.)

---

19. At equilibrium, which would be present in higher concentration
    ATP or ADP?

    ADP

---

20. CH_4 + $2O_2$ ⇌ CO_2 + $2H_2O$ + 213 Cal. Which reaction (right or left)
    has the greatest E_A? At equilibrium, would CH_4 or CO_2 be present
    in the greatest concentration?

    ----

    left
    CO_2

---

21. H_2 + I_2 + 230 cal. ⇌ 2HI (I = iodine). At equilibrium, which is
    present in higher concentration, H_2 or HI?

    H_2

---

22. A catalyst lowers the activation energy for a reaction. In the plot of item 11, would a catalyst shift E_A to the right or left? Would a catalyst affect the rate of the reaction to the right? Would a catalyst affect the rate of the reaction to the left? The effects of a catalyst on the rates to the right and left are exactly the same. Would a catalyst affect the equilibrium concentrations of the reactants and products?

Left, yes, yes, no (a catalyst alters the rate at which a reaction reaches equilibrium — but not the equilibrium concentrations.)

23. An enzyme is a biological catalyst. What is the effect of an enzyme on a chemical reaction?

An enzyme lowers the energy of activation for the reaction. (It increases the right and left rates equally.) (or similar response)

24. Would an enzyme facilitate (speed up) the attainment of equilibrium? Explain your answer.

Yes. An enzyme increases the rate of both the right and left reactions, thus facilitating the attainment of equilibrium.

25. Enzymes act by combining with or binding the reacting (*substrate*) molecules. Which group of biochemical compounds you have studied (carbohydrates, proteins, lipids, or nucleic acids) has the greatest general capacity for reacting with other molecules?

Proteins — (Indeed, *all enzymes are proteins*.)

26. Oversimplified diagram: $ADP + Ph \rightleftharpoons ATP + H_2O$
$$(A-P-P + P \rightleftharpoons A-P-P-P + H_2O)$$

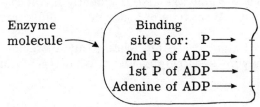

Enzyme
molecule

Binding
sites for: P⟶
2nd P of ADP⟶
1st P of ADP⟶
Adenine of ADP⟶

The enzyme binds the substrate molecules. Show how A— P— P
(ADP) and P (Ph) could be bound to the labeled binding sites of the
enzyme surface to facilitate bonding between the ADP and Ph.

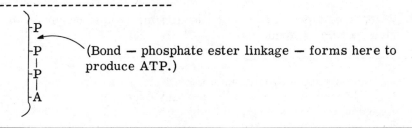

-P
-P
|
-P
|
-A

(Bond — phosphate ester linkage — forms here to
produce ATP.)

---

27. How does an enzyme lower the energy of activation for a reaction?

The enzyme binds the substrate molecules in close physical contact, thus facilitating bonding (either making or breaking of the
bond). (or similar response)

---

28. Many enzymes contain non-protein metal containing groups (e.g.
Fe and Mg). What general term would you apply to these metal-
containing groups? What would you call a protein which contains
such a group?

Prosthetic group
A conjugated protein

---

29. Many types of enzyme-substrate bonding involve ionic bonding (complexing) with metal ions of a prosthetic group. The NH_2 groups of lysine and arginine are also frequently involved in enzyme-substrate bonds. What type of bonds do you think might be involved here?

   The R groups of alanine, valine, leucine, and isoleucine are also involved in enzyme-substrate bonding. What types of bonds might this represent?

   Hydrogen bonds
   Hydrophobic bonds

---

30. What three types of bonds are usually involved in enzyme-substrate complex formation?

   Metal complexing (ionic bonds) ⎫
   H bonds   ⎬ any order
   Hydrophobic bonds   ⎭

---

31. In your own words, what is the function and mode of action of an enzyme? (Give as complete a response as you can.)

   An enzyme alters the rate of a reaction and facilitates the attainment of equilibrium without changing the equilibrium concentrations. Enzymes alter the energy of activation by binding the substrates in close physical contact, which facilitates bonding changes Enzyme-substrate bonding involves ionic (metal-complexing), hydrogen, and hydrophobic bonding. (or similar response)

Take at least a 5-minute break before continuing on to the next unit.

Again, check your retention level and review the appropriate items. Go on to the first item.

---

1. Diagram the structure of a fat composed of:

$$C_{17}H_{35}C\overset{\displaystyle O}{\underset{\displaystyle OH}{}}$$ (stearic acid)

(use the empirical formula)

- -

$$
\begin{array}{l}
\overset{\displaystyle H}{\underset{\displaystyle |}{}} \quad \overset{\displaystyle O}{\underset{\displaystyle \parallel}{}} \\
H-\overset{|}{C}-O-\overset{\parallel}{C}-C_{17}H_{35} \\
\quad\;\; | \qquad \overset{\displaystyle O}{\underset{\displaystyle \parallel}{}} \\
H-\overset{|}{C}-O-\overset{\parallel}{C}-C_{17}H_{35} \\
\quad\;\; | \qquad \overset{\displaystyle O}{\underset{\displaystyle \parallel}{}} \\
H-\overset{|}{C}-O-\overset{\parallel}{C}-C_{17}H_{35} \\
\quad\;\; \overset{|}{H}
\end{array}
$$

(stearin — beef fat)   *Review: Unit 11, Items 1-11*

187

2. Using the structural formula of stearin from the preceding item, modify it to diagram the general structure of a phospholipid. Use R_S = the H_2O soluble group.

$$\begin{array}{c}
\overset{\displaystyle H}{|} \qquad \overset{\displaystyle O}{\parallel} \\
H-C-O-C-C_{17}H_{35} \\
|\qquad\quad O \\
|\qquad\quad \parallel \\
H-C-O-C-C_{17}H_{35} \\
|\qquad\quad O \\
|\qquad\quad \parallel \\
H-C-O-P-R_S \\
\overset{\displaystyle |}{H}\qquad \overset{\displaystyle |}{OH}
\end{array}$$

(Or similar structure)

Review: Unit 11, Items 12-15

---

3. Diagram the structure of a biological membrane. Label the two major components (type of chemical compound involved).

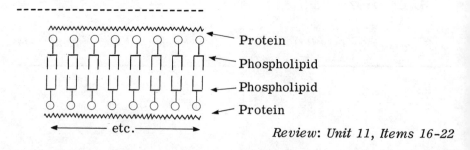

Protein

Phospholipid

Phospholipid

Protein

◄──── etc.────►

Review: Unit 11, Items 16-22

4. Diagram the basic ring structure of a steroid.

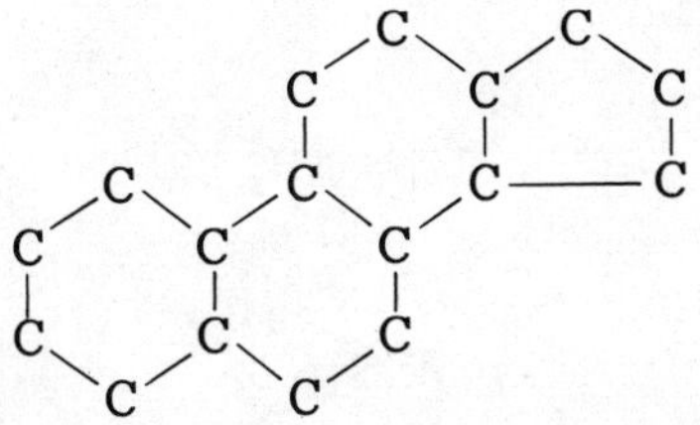

----

or

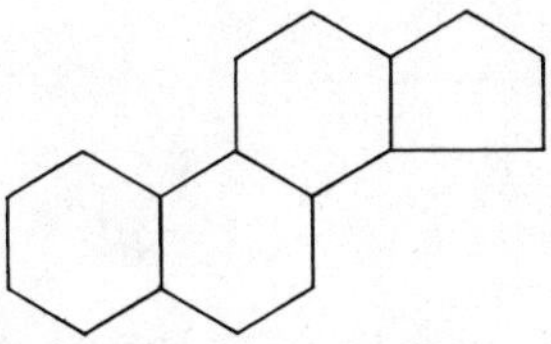

Review: Unit 11, Items 23-25

---

5. What are three major biological functions of sterols?

As hormones, membrane structure, and bile sterol (cholesterol).
Review: Unit 11, Items 25-31

---

6. Label each of the following N-bases as a purine or pyrimidine.

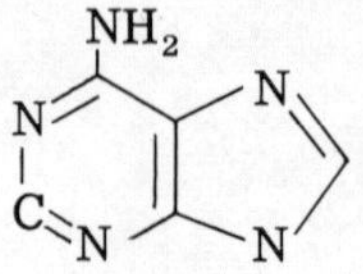

Adenine 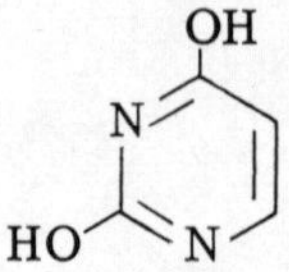   Uracil 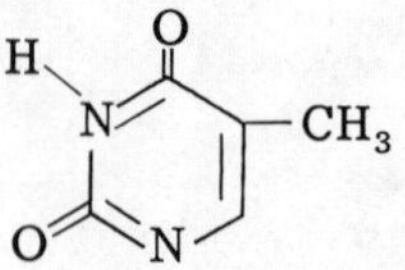   Thymine

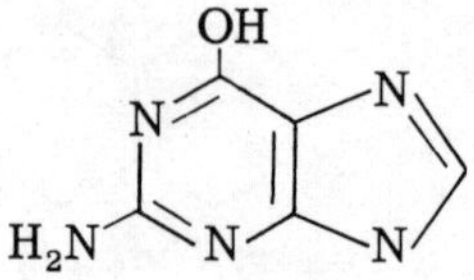

Guanine 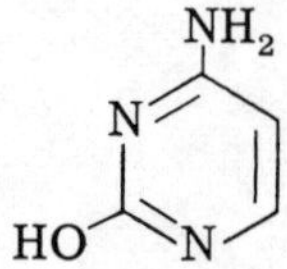   Cytosine

- -

Adenine — purine   Guanine — purine
Uracil — pyrimidine   Cytosine — pyrimidine
Thymine — pyrimidine

Review: *Unit 12, Items 1-3*

---

7. What are the three components of which a nucleotide is composed?

- -

N-base (purine or pyrimidine)
Pentose sugar (ribose or deoxyribose)
Phosphate
   (any order)   *Review*: *Unit 12, Items 3-10*

---

8. Write the complementary half of this DNA chain. Include all H
bonds (:::) or (⁞⁞⁞). Circle each nucleotide in the entire molecule.

```
P— D— P— D— P— D— P— D— P— D— P— D
    |      |      |      |      |      |
    C      G      C      A      C      T
```

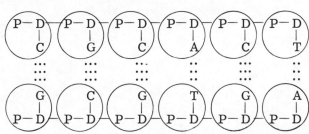

Review: Unit 12, Items 11-23

---

9. RNA *does not* (usually) form a double stranded helix. RNA can be
manufactured in the cell from genetic DNA. Construct the RNA
complement to the following genetic DNA strand: Circle each
nucleotide.

```
— P— D— P— D— P— D— P— D— P— D— P— D— P— D—
     |      |      |      |      |      |      |
     A      T      G      A      C      C      T
```

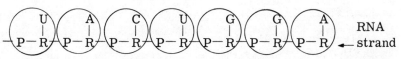

Review: Unit 12, Items 24-27

10. What name is applied to the model for the molecular structure of DNA?

Watson-Crick double helix

---

11. Write the shorthand structural formula for ATP. What is the chief function of ATP?

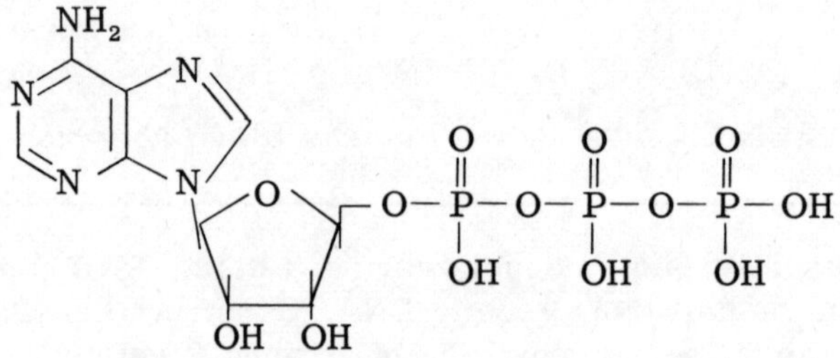

ATP functions in biological energy transfer.

Review: Unit 12, Items 29-34

---

12. Complete the following equations:
$$AMP + Ph \rightleftharpoons \quad + $$
$$ATP + H_2O \rightleftharpoons \quad + Ph$$
$$AMP + 2Ph \rightleftharpoons \quad + $$

$$AMP + Ph \rightleftharpoons ADP + H_2O$$
$$ATP + H_2O \rightleftharpoons ADP + Ph$$
$$AMP + 2Ph \rightleftharpoons ATP + 2H_2O$$

Review: Unit 12, Items 35-36

13. What groups would be particularly involved in the H bonding between a basic protein and the *backbone* of a nucleic acid?

Protein: $-$ H from NH$_2$ groups

Nucleic Acids: $=$O from $-\overset{\overset{\displaystyle O}{\|}}{\underset{\underset{\displaystyle OH}{|}}{P}}-$

Review: *Unit 12, Items 37 and 38*

---

14. What are the structural units of the nucleic acids?

Nucleotides

---

15. Write out the full name for DNA and RNA.

DNA = deoxyribose nucleic acid
RNA = ribose nucleic acid

---

16. Define briefly potential energy and kinetic energy.

Potential energy is restrained energy which can be available to do work upon removal of the restraint. Kinetic energy is the energy of motion. (or similar response)

Review: *Unit 13, Items 1-2*

---

17. How many Calories does 5000 calories equal?
    How many calories does 176 Calories equal?
    How many Calories does 162 calories equal?

----

    5   176,000 $0.162 \left(\dfrac{162}{1000} \right)$

Review: Unit 13, Items 3-6

---

18. Label each of the following reactions as either exothermic or
    endothermic.
    A. Pyruvic acid + $3O_2 \rightleftharpoons 3CO_2 + 3H_2O$
    B. $C_4H_6O_4 \rightleftharpoons C_4H_4O_4 + 2(H)$
    C. Nucleotides $\rightleftharpoons$ DNA chain
    D. AMP + 2Ph $\rightleftharpoons$ ATP
    E. Glucose + Fructose $\rightleftharpoons$ Sucrose

    A. Exothermic
    B. Exothermic
    C. Endothermic
    D. Endothermic
    E. Endothermic   *Review: Unit 13, Items 7-10*

---

19. $CH_4 + 2O_2 \rightleftharpoons CO_2 + 2H_2O + 213$ Cal. At equilibrium, would CH_4 or
    CO_2 be present in the greatest concentration?

    CO_2 *Review: Unit 13, Items 11-21*

---

20. How does an enzyme lower the energy of activation for a reaction?

    The enzyme binds the substrate molecules in close physical con-
    tact, thus facilitating bonding (either making or breaking of the
    bond). (or similar response)

Review: Unit 13, Items 22-27

21. What three types of bonds are usually involved in enzyme-substrate complex formation?

- -

Metal complexing (ionic bonds) ⎫
H bonds   ⎬ (any order)
Hydrophobic bonds   ⎭

Review: Unit 13, Items 28-30

Take at least a 5-minute break before continuing with the next unit.

UNIT *14* BIOLOGICAL CORRELATIONS

This unit provides a brief review of the major biological correlations of the molecules studied.

---

1. To what chemical group do all enzymes belong? What is glycogen?

- -

Proteins
Glycogen is a small (15 ± monosaccharide units) polysaccharide which functions in animal food storage.

---

2. What are the two *chief* components of biological membranes? What is one other constituent?

- -

Proteins ⎫
Phospholipids ⎬ (any order)
Sterols ⎭

---

3. What is the chief physiological function of ATP (and ADP)?

- -

Biological energy transfer.

---

4. Of what type of chemical material is each of the following composed? Example: Muscle — protein.
   Plant cell wall
   Arthropod exoskeleton
   Hair
   Silk
   Genes
   Leather (collagen)
   Plant starch

   Plant cell wall — carbohydrate (cellulose)
   Arthropod exoskeleton — carbohydrate derivative (chitin) (glucosamine units)
   Hair — protein (keratin)
   Silk — protein (fibrin)
   Genes — DNA
   Leather (collagen) — protein
   Plant starch — carbohydrate

5. What type of protein is usually found H-bonded to the DNA of the chromosomes?

   Basic protein

You will probably find it helpful to work thru each of the three review sections again to check your retention. You may go over them rapidly if you remember the material, but be careful to check back and review areas in which your retention is weak.

UNIT *S-1* *MOLECULAR WEIGHT,*
LABORATORY SOLUTION PREPARATION

Material Covered

Atomic weight
Molecular weight
Preparation of molar solutions
Balancing equations
Water of hydration

Eventually most biologists get their hands dirty mixing laboratory solutions. Here's how. (Use Panel C for this unit.)

---

1. What are the *three* fundamental particles of which all atoms are constituted?

   Protons, electrons, neutrons (any order).

---

2. How many protons and electrons does the Al atom contain?
   _____ protons
   _____ electrons

----

   13 protons
   13 electrons

PANEL C *Atomic Weights*

(Use with unit S-1)

Element	Atomic Number	Atomic Weight
Hydrogen	1	1.0
Helium	2	4.0
Lithium	3	6.9
Beryllium	4	9.0
Boron	5	10.8
Carbon	6	12.0
Nitrogen	7	14.0
Oxygen	8	16.0
Fluorine	9	19.0
Neon	10	20.1
Sodium	11	23.0
Magnesium	12	24.3
Aluminum	13	27.0
Silicon	14	28.1
Phosphorus	15	31.0
Sulfur	16	32.1
Chlorine	17	35.5
Argon	18	39.9
Potassium	19	39.1
Calcium	20	40.1

PANEL D *Two-Place Logarithms*

Number	Logarithms
1	0.00
2	0.30
3	0.48
4	0.60
5	0.70
6	0.78
7	0.85
8	0.90
9	0.95

Memorization Table

$\log 2 = 0.3$
$\log 3 = 0.5$
$\log 5 = 0.7$
$\log 8 = 0.9$

3. | | Calcium |
    | -------------------------- | ------- |
    | Atomic weight | 40 |
    | Minus the number of protons| -20 |
    | Number of neutrons | 20 |

How many neutrons are there in an F atom?

----

10 neutrons $(19 - 9)$

4. What does the atomic weight of an atom equal (in terms of funda-
    mental particles)?

Number of protons + Number of neutrons. (This is only a *rough*
approximation, since natural substances may be composed of
isotopic mixtures.)

5. Most chlorine atoms contain
    _____ protons
    _____ electrons
    _____ neutrons

----

17 protons
17 electrons
18 neutrons (Actually in the natural mixture about half contain 18
and half 19.)

6. M.W. = molecular weight
    A. W. = atomic weight

    M.W. (HCl) = A.W. (H) + A.W. (Cl) = 1.0 + 35.5 = 36.5
    M.W. ($CaCl_2$) = A.W. (Ca) + A.W. (Cl) + A.W. (Cl) = 40.1 + 35.5 +
                      35.5 = 111.1
    M.W. (NaOH) =

40.0
M.W. (NaOH) = A.W. (Na) + A.W. (O) + A.W. (H) = 23.0 + 16.0 +
              1.0 = 40.0

7. M.W. (NaOH) = 40.0
   Gram molecular weight (NaOH) = 40.0 grams
   What is the *molecular weight* and the *gram molecular weight* of
   K_2SO_4?

   174.3
   174.3 grams

---

8. A solution of 1 *molar concentration* contains 1 *gram molecular
   weight per liter of solution.*
   Thus: 1 M. = 1 G.M.W/liter
          0.1 M. = 0.1 G.M.W/liter
   How many grams of NaOH would 1 liter of a 1 M solution contain?

   ----

   40 grams

---

9. How many grams of NaOH would 1 liter of an 0.3 M solution contain?

   12.0 grams (40.0 g. × 0.3 M)

---

10. How many grams of NaOH would 400 ml. of a 1 M solution con-
    tain?

    (1 ml. = 1 milliliter = $\dfrac{1}{1000}$ liter)

    (1000 ml. = 1 l.)

    16.0 grams ($40.0 \times \dfrac{400}{1000} = 40.0 \times 0.4$)

---

11. How many grams of NaOH would 600 ml. of a 0.2 M solution contain?

4.8 grams
   G.M.W. = 40 g.
   1 liter 1 M = 40 g./liter
   1 liter 0.2 M = 8 g./liter
   600 ml 0.2 M = 4.8 g./600 ml.

---

12. *Volumetric flasks* are used in the preparation of solutions.

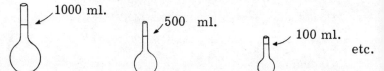

1000 ml.   500 ml.   100 ml.
                                             etc.

The *chemical* to be dissolved is placed in the appropriate flask.
Distilled water is then added until flask is three-quarters full.
The flask is *swirled* until all the chemical is dissolved. Then distilled water is added to the volume mark. List the steps in preparing a 1 M solution of NaOH.

Calculate: 1 liter 1 M NaOH = 40 g./liter
Use a 1-liter volumetric flask. Weigh out 40 grams of NaOH.
Add about 800 ml. distilled H_2O. Swirl flask until all NaOH is
dissolved. Add distilled water to the 1000-ml. line. (or similar
outline)

13. Outline the procedure you would follow in the preparation of 500 ml. of a 0.30 M solution of $NaHCO_3$.

Calculate: 1 liter 1.00 M $NaHCO_3$ = 84.0 g./liter
            1 liter 0.30 M $NaHCO_3$ = 25.20 g./liter
            500 ml. 0.30 M $NaHCO_3$ = 12.60 g./500 ml.
Obtain a 500-ml. volumetric flask. Weigh out 12.60 grams of $NaHCO_3$. Add about 400 ml. distilled water. Swirl flask until all $NaHCO_3$ is dissolved. Add distilled water to the 500 ml. line. (or similar outline)

---

14. Some crystalline materials contain *water of hydration* in the crystal structure. This is *included* in the calculation of the molecular weight. What is the molecular weight of $MgCl_2 \cdot 6H_2O$?

203

Calculation: Mg $-$ 24.3 $\times$ 1 = 24.3
              Cl $-$ 35.5 $\times$ 2 = 71.0
              H $-$ 1.0 $\times$ 12 = 12.0
              O $-$ 16.0 $\times$ 6 = 96.0
                                     203.3

---

15. How many grams of $MgCl_2 \cdot 6H_2O$ would you use in preparing 1 liter of a 0.1 M solution?

20.3 g./liter

Take at least a 5-minute break before continuing with the next unit.

UNIT *S-2* PH

The biological activity of many cellular constituents, particularly enzymes and other proteins, is greatly influenced by changes in pH. The pH of a solution will be related to hydrogen ion concentration and defined. For those who need it or who desire it, there is a brief review of logarithms. You will then learn to calculate the pH from the molarity of a solution of acid or base, and vice versa. Buffer systems will be studied and you will learn how to choose a buffer for experimental purposes.

Material Covered

Acidic — basic.
Logarithms (brief introduction).
Definition of pH.
Calculation of pH from normality of strong acid.
Calculation of pH from normality of strong base.
Buffer system.
Buffer capacity.
Henderson-Hasselbach equation.
Choice of buffer for a specific pH.

1.

H$^+$ Concentration	pH	Acidity	Basicity
0.1 M.	1	High	Low
0.001 M.	3	High	Low
0.000001 M.	6	High	Low
0.0000001 M.	7	Neutral	Neutral
0.00000001 M.	8	Low	High
0.00000000001 M.	11	Low	High
0.0000000000001 M.	13	Low	High

If acidity is high basicity is_____.
If acidity is high pH is _____.
High [H$^+$] = _____ pH. ([ ] = concentration; [H$^+$] = H$^+$
concentration).
Low [H$^+$] = _____ pH.

Low, low, low, high.

---

2. What does the symbol "[OH$^-$]" mean?

OH$^-$ *concentration*

---

3. Complete this equation for the dissociation of HCl:
   HCl (aq) →

HCl (aq) → H$^+$ (aq) + Cl$^-$ (aq)

---

4. HCl dissociates completely in dilute aqueous solutions. Which of
   the following solutions is the most *acid*?
       0.1 M. HCl
       0.01 M. HCl
       0.02 M. HCl
       0.005 M. HCl
   Which is the most basic? Which has the lowest pH? Which has the
   highest pH?

0.1 M. (this has the highest H$^+$ concentration)
0.005 M.   0.1 M.   0.005 M.

206

5. Which of the following is most *basic*?
    0.6 M. HCl
    0.02 M. HCl
    0.004 M. HCl
    0.001 M. HCl
    Which has the lowest pH?

    0.001 M. HCl   0.6 M. HCl

---

6. If you are facile with logarithms you may skip to item 24. Try
    the following quiz to ascertain your facility (use Panel D):

A. 10^{-3} = _____   H. $\log \dfrac{a}{b}$ = _____
B. log 1000 = _____
C. log 0.01 = _____
D. log 30 = _____   I. $\log \dfrac{1}{x}$ = _____
E. antilog 2.7 = _____   J. from memory: log 2 = _____
F. antilog -3.3 = _____   log 3 = _____
G. log $(a \times b)$ = _____   log 5 = _____
                                                    log 8 = _____

A. 0.001 or $\dfrac{1}{1000}$ H. log a – log b
B. 3   I. $-\log x$
C. -2 J. log 2 = 0.3
D. 1.48 (or 1.5)   log 3 = 0.5
E. 500   log 5 = 0.7
F. 0.0005   log 8 = 0.9
G. log a + log b
H. log a – log b A score of 7 or more indicates
                                        reasonable facility.

7. Powers: 10^2 = 10 to the second power (or 10 squared)
               10^3 = 10 to the third power (or 10 cubed)
               10^4 = 10 to the fourth power

$10^0 = 10 \times \dfrac{1}{10} = 1$

$10^1 = 10$
$10^2 = 10 \times 10 = 100$
$10^3 = 10 \times 10 \times 10 = 1000$
$10^4 = $ _____
$10^5 = $ _____
$10^8 = $ _____

- -

10^4 = 10,000 (4 zeros)
10^5 = 100,000 (5 zeros)
10^8 = 100,000,000

---

8. The logarithm (log) of 100 is 2 (10^2 = 100) (10 raised to the 2nd
                                                         power)
    log 1000 = 3 (10^3 = 1000) (10 raised to the 3rd power)
    log 100,000 = 5   (10^5 = 100,000) (10 raised to the 5th power)
    What is the logarithm of a number ?

- -

The log of a number is the power to which 10 must be raised to
give the number. (or similar response)

---

9. log 100 = _____
    log 10,000 = _____
    log 10,000,000 = _____

- -

2, 4, 7

2

08   CONCEPTS IN BIOCHEMISTRY

10. $10^0 = 10 \times \dfrac{1}{10} = 1$

$10^{-1} = 10 \times \dfrac{1}{10} \times \dfrac{1}{10} = 0.1$ (decimal point moved over 1 place)

$10^{-2} = \dfrac{1}{10} \times \dfrac{1}{10} = 0.01$ (decimal point moved over 2 places)

$10^{-3} = \dfrac{1}{10} \times \dfrac{1}{10} \times \dfrac{1}{10} = 0.001$ (decimal point moved over 3 places)

$\log 0.01 = -2$

$\log 0.001 = $ _____

$\log 0.00001 = $ _____

$-3, -5$

---

11. $\log (a \times b) = \log a + \log b$

$\log 20 = \log (2 \times 10) = $ _____

$\log 10 = 1$

But, what is the log of 20? Then look up log 2 in Panel D, and solve the problem.

$\log 20 = \log (2 \times 10) = \log 2 + \log 10$

1.3 $(\log 2 + \log 10 = 0.3 + 1.0)$

---

12. What is $\log 500$?

$\log 500 = 2.70$ (Calculation: $\log 500 = \log 5 + \log 100$

                                                    $= 0.70 + 2$

                                                    $= 2.70)$

---

13. What is $\log 0.3$? (Solve as you did the last item.)

$\log 0.3 = -0.5$ [Calculation: $\log 0.3 = \log 3 + \log 0.1$

                                           $= 0.5 + (-1)$

                                           $= 0.5 - 1$

                                           $= -0.5]$

14. What is $\log 0.0008$?

$\log 0.0008 = -3.1$ [Calculation: $\log 0.0008 = \log 8 + \log 0.0001$
$$= 0.9 + (-4)$$
$$= -3.1]$$

---

15. $\log(?) = 2$ (*anti*log of $2 = ?$)
What is the antilog of 5?
$\log(?) = -3$

100; 100,000; 0.001

---

16. $\log(?) = 2.78$
What is the antilog of 3.85?

----

600   (Calculation: $\log(?) = 2.78$
$$= 2 + 0.78$$
$$? = 100 \times 6$$
$$? = 600$$

7000 $\log ? = 3.85 = 3 + 0.85$
$$? = 1000 \times 7)$$

---

17. What is the antilog of -2.3?

0.005   (Calculation: $\log ? = -2.3$
$$= -3 + 0.7$$
$$? = 10^{-3} \times 5$$
$$? = 0.005)$$

18. $\log (?) = -4.05$

0.00009   (Calculation: $\log (?) = -4.05$
$$= -5 + 0.95$$
$$? = 10^{-5} \times 0.9$$
$$? = 0.00009)$$

---

19. *Without* consulting Panel H:

     $\log 8 =$ _____
     $\log 3 =$ _____
     $\log 2 =$ _____
     $\log 5 =$ _____

$\log 8 = 0.9$ $\log 2 = 0.3$
$\log 3 = 0.5$ $\log 5 = 0.7$ (memorize these!)

---

20. Also: $\log \dfrac{a}{b} = \log a - \log b$

What is $\log \dfrac{1}{2}$?

$\log \dfrac{1}{2} = \log 1 - \log 2 = 0 - 0.3$
$$= -0.3$$

---

21. What is $\log \dfrac{1}{a}$?

$\log \dfrac{1}{a} = -\log a$ (Calculation: $\log \dfrac{1}{a} = \log 1 - \log a = 0 - \log a$
$$= -\log a)$$

---

22. What is $\log \dfrac{1}{[H^+]}$?

$$\log \frac{1}{[H^+]} = -\log [H^+]$$

---

23. Repeat the logarithm quiz (item 6).

---

24. The symbol p = the negative logarithm
$$= -\log.$$
Thus, what is the pH $(p[H^+])$?

$-\log [H^+]$ (The negative logarithm of the hydrogen ion concentration.)

---

25. Define pH.

$$pH = -\log [H^+] \left(or = \log \frac{1}{[H^+]}\right)$$

---

26. What is the pH of a 0.01 M HCl solution?

----

pH = 2 $pH = -\log [H^+]$
$$= -\log 0.01 = -\log - 10^{-2}$$
$$= -(-2) = 2$$

---

27. What is the pH of a 0.005 M HCl solution?

----

pH = 2.3 $\quad$ [Calculation: $pH = \log \dfrac{1}{[H^+]} = \log \dfrac{1}{0.005}$

$$= \log \dfrac{1}{5 \times 10^{-3}} = \log \left(\dfrac{1}{5} \times \dfrac{1}{10^{-3}} \right)$$
$$= \log (0.2 \times 10^3) = \log (2 \times 10^2)$$
$$= \log 2 + \log 10^2$$
$$= 0.3 + 2 = 2.3]$$

28. What is the pH of a 0.000005 M solution of H_2SO_4? (Note: each H_2SO_4 dissociates to produce $2H^+$.)

----

pH = 5 $\quad$ [Calculation: $pH = \log \dfrac{1}{[H^+]} = \log \dfrac{1}{0.00001}$
0.000005 M H_2SO_4
$\quad$ = 0.00001 M H^+ $\qquad\qquad$ $= \log \dfrac{1}{10^{-5}} = \log 10^5$

$\qquad\qquad\qquad\qquad\qquad\qquad\qquad\qquad$ $= 5]$

29. In water solutions, $H_2O \rightleftharpoons H^+ (aq) + OH^- (aq)$. If $[H^+]$ is increased, what effect will this have on $[OH^-]$?

$[OH^-]$ will decrease $(H_2O \rightleftharpoons H^+ + OH^-)$ (Review: Unit 5)

30. This relationship between $[H^+]$ and $[OH^-]$ can be expressed by the equation: pH + pOH = 14.
If the pOH is 3.0, what is pH?

----

pH = 11

31. Complete the equation for the dissociation of NaOH:

NaOH(aq) →

NaOH dissociates completely in water. What is the pOH of a 0.01 M. solution of NaOH?

$NaOH(aq) \rightarrow Na^+ (aq) + OH^- (aq)$
pOH = 2

---

32. What is the *pH* of a 0.1 M. solution of NaOH?

----

pH = 13   (pOH = 1; pH + pOH = 14;
                                          pH = 14 − 1 = 13)

---

33. How would you prepare 1 liter of a solution of NaOH which would have a pH of 12.7?

One-liter volumetric flask. Use 2.0 g. NaOH. Add 800 ml. distilled H_2O. Swirl until dissolved. Add distilled H_2O to mark.
Sample calculation: pH + pOH = 14
                              12.7 + pOH = 14
                                    pOH = 1.3

$$pOH = \log \frac{1}{[OH^-]} = 1.3$$
$$= 0.3 + 1$$
$$= \log 2 + \log 10$$
$$= \log (2 \times 10) = \log (0.2 \times 10^2)$$
$$= \log \frac{1}{5} \times \frac{1}{10^{-2}} = \log \frac{1}{5 \times 10^{-2}}$$

$OH^- = 0.05$ M
M.W. = 40.0
0.05 M = 2 g./liter

34. H_2O (d) $\rightleftharpoons H^+$ (aq) $+ OH^-$ (aq). What is the pH of distilled H_2O?

----

pH = 7

[Calculation: $[H^+] = [OH^-]$
pH = pOH
pH + pOH = 14
2pH = 14
pH = 7]

---

35. HAc = Acetic Acid = a "weak" acid.
Ac^- = Acetate Ion (salt ion)
$HAc(aq) \rightleftharpoons H^+(aq) + Ac^-(aq)$

(10,000) $\longrightarrow$ (1) $\longrightarrow$ (1)

Proportion of molecules and ions at equilibrium.

∴ HAc is "weakly" dissociated.
HCl dissociates completely.
Is it a weak or a strong acid?

Strong

---

36. $HAc(aq) \rightleftharpoons H^+(aq) + Ac^-(aq)$.
If base (OH^-) is added, with which component of the above reaction would the (OH^-) react?

$H^+(aq)$ $[H^+(aq) + OH^-(aq) \rightleftharpoons H_2O]$

---

37. $HAc(aq) \rightleftharpoons H^+(aq) + Ac^-(aq)$
If acid (H^+) is added, with which component of the above reaction would the (H^+) react?

$Ac^-(aq)$ $[HAc(aq) \rightleftharpoons H^+(aq) + Ac^-(aq)$; as $H^+(aq)$ is increased]

---

38. Weak Acid (aq) $\rightleftharpoons$ H$^+$(aq) + Salt Anion$^-$ (aq)

This is a *buffer* system — it buffers or resists a change in pH. As pH is *increased* does H$^+$ or OH$^-$ increase? Which component of the buffer system resists this change? As pH is *decreased* does H$^+$ or OH$^-$ increase? Which component of the buffer system resists this change?

OH$^-$ increases   H$^+$ increases
H$^+$ (reacts with the OH$^-$)   Salt anion$^-$ (reacts with the H$^+$)

---

39. What are the components of a buffer system? How does a buffer system function?

Weak acid + Salt anion (of the weak acid)
The buffer system resists a change in pH.
   (H$^+$ reacts with OH$^-$.)
   (Salt anion reacts with H$^+$.)

---

40. A weak acid dissociates only slightly. Would it produce much salt anion?

The *buffer capacity* (salt anion) against [H$^+$] can be increased by adding a salt (e.g., sodium acetate) which dissociates completely in water. In the buffer system:

$$HAc(aq) \rightleftharpoons H^+ (aq) + Ac^- (aq) + Na^+ (aq) \leftarrow NaAc (aq)$$

Does the H$^+$ come predomi-   Does the Ac$^-$ come predomi-
nantly from the weak acid   nantly from the weak acid or
or from the salt?   from the salt?

No
H$^+$ comes from the weak acid
Ac$^-$ comes from the salt

---

41. If a buffer system (composed of a weak acid and its salt) is to resist changes in pH by acids and bases with equal effectiveness, what should be the relationship between the acid and salt concentrations?

They should be equal.

---

42. Of what components would an efficient buffer system be composed?

A weak acid and its salt *in equal concentrations.*

---

43. The relationship between the pH and the relative concentrations of weak acid and salt can be expressed by the *Henderson-Hasselbach equation*:

$$pH = pK + \log \frac{[\text{Salt}]}{[\text{Acid}]} \qquad \text{where} \qquad$$ pK = the $-$ log of the *dissociation constant* of the weak acid*

What does the symbol "[acid]" mean? What does the symbol "[salt]" mean?

*The dissociation constant for any weak acid can be found in the *Handbook of Chemistry* (see index under "dissociation constants — acids and bases").

[Acid] = the concentration of the weak acid
[Salt] = the concentration of the salt of the weak acid.

---

44. *Henderson-Hasselbach equation:*

$$pH = pK + \log \frac{[Salt]}{[Acid]}$$

What does pH = if [Acid] = [Salt] ?

$pH = pK$ (pH = pK + log $\frac{[Salt]}{[Acid]}$ [Acid] = [Salt]

$pH = pK + \log 1$ $\frac{[Salt]}{[Acid]} = 1$

$pH = pK + 0$

$pH = pK$)

---

45. What is the relationship between [Acid] and [Salt] when the *buffer capacity* is greatest? Under these conditions, what is the relationship between pH and pK? For the greatest buffer capacity, the pH should = _____.

[Acid] = [Salt]

pH = pK

pK

---

46. Write the Henderson-Hasselbach equation.

$$pH = pK + \log \frac{[Salt]}{[Acid]}$$

---

47. What is the name of this equation?

$$pH = pK + \log \frac{[Salt]}{[Acid]}$$

Henderson-Hasselbach equation.

---

48. For the maximal buffer capacity at pH = 4.7, which of the following weak acids would you choose?

	pK
Phosphoric	2.1
Acetic	4.8
Carbonic	6.4

Explain your choice.

Acetic
pK is closest to desired pH
   (4.8 as compared to 4.7)
   (pK = pH for maximal buffer capacity)

REVIEW – UNITS S-1 AND S-2

1. A potassium atom contains _____ protons; _____ electrons; _____ neutrons.

    19, 19, 21   *Review*: *Unit S-1, Items 1-5*

---

2. What is the gram molecular weight of Mg_2SO_4 ?

    144.7 grams   *Review*: *Unit S-1, Items 6-7*

---

3. How many grams of NaF would 500 ml. of a 0.2 molar solution contain?

    4.2 grams   *Review*: *Unit S-1, Items 8-11*

---

4. Outline the procedure you would follow in the preparation of 100 ml. of a 0.7 M. solution of $CaCl_2$.

---

gram M.W. $CaCl_2$ = 111.1 grams
100 ml. of a 0.7 M. $CaCl_2$ = 7.777 g/100 ml.
Obtain a 100 ml. volumetric flask.
Weigh out 7.707 g. of $CaCl_2$. Place it in the flask.
Add about 80 ml. of distilled water; swirl until all the $CaCl_2$ is dissolved.
Add distilled water to the 100 ml. line of the flask.
(Or similar response)   *Review: Unit S-1, Items 12-13*

---

5. How many grams of $MnSO_4 \cdot 4H_2O$ would you use to prepare a liter of a 1 M. solution? (atomic weight of Mn = 54.9)

---

223 grams   *Review: Unit S-1, Items 14-15*

---

6. Repeat the logarithm quiz in Unit S-2, Item 6.

---

7. Write a definition of pH.

$$pH = -\log(H^+) \text{ or } pH = \log \frac{1}{(H^+)}$$ *Review: Unit S-2,*
                                                                          Items 1-5 and 24-25

---

8. What is the pH of a 0.001 M. solution of HCl?

---

pH = 3.0   *Review: Unit S-2, Item 26*

---

9. What is the pH of a 0.002 M. solution of HCl?

----

pH = 2.7   *Review: Unit S-2, Items 27-28*

---

10. What is the pH of a 0.005 M. solution of NaOH?

----

pH = 11.7   *Review: Unit S-2, Items 29-33*

---

11. What are the components of a buffer system? Explain how a buffer system resists changes in pH.

Weak acid + salt anion (of the weak acid)
H^+ from the weak acid combines with excess OH^-
Salt anion (from a salt of the weak acid) combines with excess H^+.
                                                   Review: Unit S-2, Items 34-42

---

12. Write the Henderson-Hasselbach equation.

$$pH = pK + \log \frac{(salt)}{(acid)}$$ *Review: Unit S-2, Items 43-46*

---

13. For maximum buffering effectiveness at pH = 6.5, which of the
    following weak acids would you choose? Explain your choice.

	pK
phosphoric	2.1
acetic	4.8
carbonic	6.4

    What else would you need to prepare the buffer system?

    ----

    carbonic   The pK is closest to the desired pH.
    A salt of carbonic acid (such as sodium bicarbonate).

                                          Review: Unit S-2, Items 47-48

Additional Review: If you desire additional review, you may repeat the
four review units plus Unit 14. The review units have been constructed
to cover all the major concepts and objectives of the text.